D1062707

AFTER-DINNER SCIENCE

Books by Kenneth M. Swezey

AFTER-DINNER SCIENCE
SCIENCE MAGIC
CHEMISTRY MAGIC

AFTER-DINNER SCIENCE

R E V I S E D   E D I T I O N

K E N N E T H   M.   S W E Z E Y

Photographs by the author

j 507

McGraw-Hill BOOK COMPANY, INC. *New York   Toronto   London*

Printed in the United States of America

WHAT IT'S ALL ABOUT

This is a book for anyone, young or old, who wants to know more about the workings of the world of science in which he lives and who wants to have fun while doing it.

After-dinner Science is a book of *experiences*, rather than a book merely to be read. It is a book of scientific adventures in which you can learn many of the fundamental principles of physics and chemistry by actually demonstrating them.

Most of the great scientists of history recognized the value of simple and dramatic demonstrations. The first steam engine on record, the *aeolipile*, a toy exhibited by Heron of Alexandria more than 100 b.c., is described perennially in modern textbooks, while a model of it is being used today by a big engineering company to demonstrate the principle of jet-propelled aircraft. Merely by dropping weights from the Leaning Tower of Pisa. Galileo helped to revolutionize the scientific thought of his day. The toy "Bottle Imp" of Descartes is now better remembered than that great man's philosophy.

The truth is that we learn the most from and remember best those facts that amaze us, amuse us, or that give us a new light on the simple experiences of daily living.

In the present book the author has tried to utilize this formula —to make sound science more palatable by means of experiments that amaze, amuse, or that answer everyday questions about which the reader is already curious. Some of these have been adapted from the works of the great classic scientists. Some illustrate the science behind practical problems of living. Others attempt to demonstrate the basic principles of science in the current news.

Many of the experiments are so simple and produce such astonishing results that they might be used to spark the conversation at the dinner table. Others might be used as stunts at the club or party. Almost all can be performed with equipment usually found around the house, and with chemicals that can be bought at the local drugstore or photographic store, if they are not already in the kitchen.

A WORD OF THANKS

Many of the photographs and part of the text of *After-Dinner Science* have appeared in *Life, The Saturday Evening Post, Collier's, Liberty, Popular Science Monthly, Skyways,* and other magazines.

To the editors of these periodicals, the author wishes to express his appreciation. In particular, he wants to thank Raymond J. Brown, under whose editorship of *Popular Science Monthly* this series of everyday demonstrations was begun; then Perry Githens, Volta Torrey, Frank Rowsome, Harry Walton, and Robert P. Stevenson, later editors, under whom it continued. He also wants to express his gratitude to Gerard Piel, formerly science editor of *Life* and now publisher of *The Scientific American,* Robert Fuoss and Arthur W. Baum of *The Saturday Evening Post,* and Gurney Williams of *Look,* for encouragement and cooperation. To Max Lowenherz of Three Lions, Incorporated, photo agency go thanks for introducing the demonstrations to the readers of many nonscientific newspapers and magazines.

Dr. Morris Meister, president of the Bronx Community College, and formerly president of the National Science Teachers Association, deserves special thanks for his kind appraisals of the author's experiments in *The Science Classroom,* over a period of many years. The author is also grateful to Dr. Harold Frediani, formerly chief chemist of Eimer and Amend, for help with chemicals and apparatus, and to Bobby and John Turner for lending him the locomotive used to illustrate the principle of action and reaction.

Heartfelt gratitude goes to the following friends who inspired some of the experiments and posed patiently for the photographs: Ray Albert, Ruby Balke, Richie Bohm, John and Alice Byrne, Richie Ciccarello, Joan Clifford, Donald Cluen, Richie Dempsey, Harry Dewdney, Gene Duffy, Dave Findlay, David Fletcher, Bill Green, Billy Halpin, Michael Hylas, Tommy and Margaret Killeen, Dan Korbelak, Jack Looney, Bob and Connie MacCrate, Billy McGarry, Billy Mutell, Richie Olszewski, Alex Puzel, and Bobby Read. Without their help the book would have been impossible.

KENNETH M. SWEZEY

CONTENTS

PROBLEMS OF GRAVITY

FORCES AND INERTIA

SOUND WAVES AND RESONANCE

It's Done with Light and Mirrors

Electricity and Magnetism

Your Senses May Fool You

Get Acquainted with Chemistry

AFTER-DINNER SCIENCE

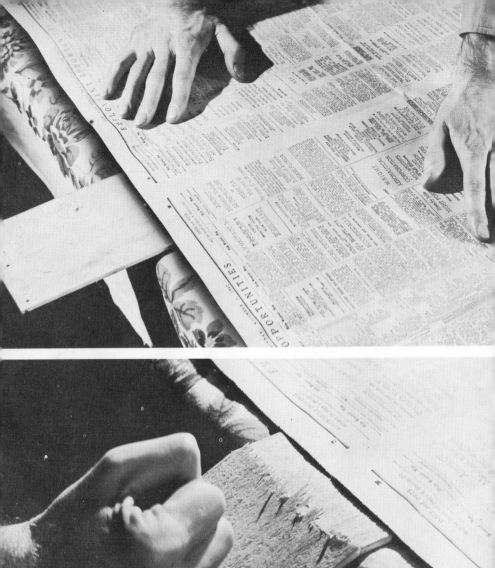
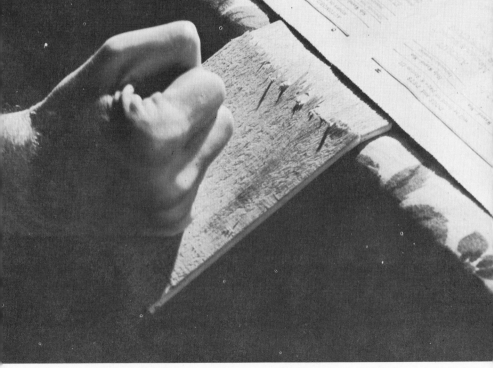

FACTS ABOUT AIR

Thin Air Is Weighty Matter

Because it is inside and under and around as well as on top of us, we are seldom conscious of the weight of air. Yet, piled high as it is in our atmosphere, air is staggeringly heavy. On every square inch of person or thing at sea level air presses down with a force of almost 15 pounds. If we were not buoyed up by the air around us, the air on our head and shoulders alone would crush us to our knees. Over the whole earth, thin air bears down with a might of more than 5,000,000,000,000,000 tons!

With a couple of sheets of newspaper and a thin piece of wood about 4 inches wide and 2 feet long, you can demonstrate dramatically the tremendous weight of air. Lay the strip on a table so that about 4 inches of the end projects over the edge. Then spread two whole double sheets of newspaper over the part of the strip that rests on the table, carefully smoothing them down so that they hug the stick and table closely.

Now take your stance and strike the end of the strip a hard, swift blow with your fist. Instead of throwing the paper to the ceiling, the stick snaps in two as if the other end were nailed to the table! Because air is unable to get under the paper fast enough to balance the air above it, the air pressure on top of the paper may be momentarily as heavy as 5 tons!

If the density of air remained constant as it extended upward, we could calculate from its pressure at sea level that the atmosphere was about 5 miles high. In reality, the density of air decreases—rapidly at first and then more slowly—as it rises from the earth. In consequence, about half of all our air lies below a height of 3½ miles and about 95 per cent below a height of 13 miles. How far the atmosphere extends above this can only be estimated. From the height of auroral displays, scientists calculate that there must be traces of air at least 600 miles above the earth.

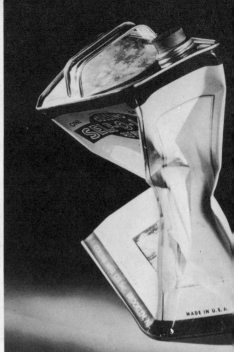

Air Pressure Crushes a Can

If your body were not composed chiefly of incompressible liquids and solids and if air did not fill the spaces between them, you would be crushed flatter than a pancake by the external pressure of the atmosphere. If all the air could suddenly be removed from inside your house, that structure would instantly be smashed to the ground.

This squeezing ability of air is easy to prove. All you need is a flat-sided gallon can and a stopper that fits it tightly. Put about ½ inch of water into the can and set the can on the stove; boil the water briskly for several minutes. Then remove the can from the heat and insert the stopper firmly as soon as the outgoing steam permits.

As the can cools, the steam inside condenses to form a partial vacuum. The air at reduced pressure inside the can soon begins to lose out against the greater pressure of the atmosphere without. Finally, amid creaks and groans, the sides of the can collapse, literally crushed in the hand of an invisible giant.

4

Boil Your Coffee with Ice

Your friends will open their eyes when they see you boiling coffee with a cake of ice. To do this, you need the bottom of a small-necked vacuum coffee maker, a cork to fit it, and an ice cube. Considerable air pressure is involved, so it's safer to use a 2- or 4-cup maker than a larger one. Leave about ½ inch of coffee in the pot and boil it until the steam drives out all the air. Then remove the pot from the heat and, as soon as the steam subsides enough, stopper tightly. When visible boiling has stopped, invert the pot and place an ice cube on the bottom. The coffee starts to boil again and continues until it's almost cold. Know why? The boiling point of water depends upon the air pressure at its surface. As the pressure is reduced, the boiling temperature is also lowered. (That's why it's harder to boil eggs or vegetables at high altitudes.) Here the ice cube lowers the pressure above the coffee by condensing the steam as fast as it is made and so produces a constant partial vacuum in the pot.

Air Pressure Works Pumps and Siphons

When you suck up water with a pump or suck up soda with a straw, you don't really *suck up* these things at all; for the water and soda are actually *pushed up* the pipe or straw by the pressure of the atmosphere!

Before 300 B.C. Aristotle started a misconception that other philosophers echoed for 2,000 years. According to these men, vacuums just couldn't exist. Nature had such a "horror" of empty spaces that it instantly filled them up with anything near at hand. Water followed the piston of a suction pump simply because Nature dreaded a void.

When someone finally discovered that no suction pump would lift water more than about 34 feet, even Galileo was astonished. His pupil Torricelli soon proved, however, that the mysterious 34 feet represented *the height of a column of water that could exactly be balanced by the pressure of the atmosphere*. Water was not *pulled* up a pipe by any mythical dread of a vacuum but was *pushed* up whenever the air pressure at the top of the pipe was reduced to less than the air pressure at the bottom by working a piston.

As siphons also depend upon air pressure, these useful devices can't lift water higher than 34 feet either. To demonstrate a siphon, half fill two glasses with water and connect them with a rubber tube, also filled with water, as shown at right. Now raise one glass above the other, and water flows mysteriously from the higher water level to the lower. Raise the other glass, and the water flows back again, never stopping until the level in both glasses is equal!

The secret? When the water level in the two glasses is equal, the downward pressure of the water in the two legs of the tube is balanced and so opposes equally the upward force of air pressure. Lower one glass, however, and the downward pressure in the leg in this glass increases because its water column (measured from water level to top of tube) is lengthened. With relatively less water pressure to buck against, air pressure in the high glass forces water over to the low glass until balance is restored.

Raise one of these glasses, connected by their simple siphon, and water flows mysteriously into the other glass—thanks to unbalanced pressure.

A Stool Is Held Up by Air

The handy "suction cups" that hold hooks to walls and help secure carrying devices to the top of your car depend also upon atmospheric pressure. When you press these cups against a smooth surface, part of the air is forced out from under them. The atmosphere then pushes them down from the outside so that they cannot fall off.

As long as air can't get between them, perfectly flat surfaces can also be held together by air pressure. To demonstrate this, tie a string to a flat sink stopper, wet its undersurface, and press it against a smooth stool top. You can now lift the stool by means of the air forcing it against the stopper.

Rusting Iron Measures the Oxygen in Air

Near sea level, the earth's atmosphere consists of a mixture of 21 per cent oxygen and 78 per cent nitrogen, with argon and traces of other inert gases making up the remaining 1 per cent. The amount of oxygen in the air can be measured roughly by wedging a wad of steel wool, moistened with vinegar to hasten the reaction, in the bottom of a tall glass and inverting the glass in a dish of water. As the iron in the steel wool rusts, it robs oxygen from the air, and water rises in the glass to take its place. In a matter of hours, the water will rise about one-fifth of the way up the glass.

BASEBALL CURVES, AIRPLANES, AND JET PROPULSION

Bernoulli's Paradox

Every time you spray insecticide on your garden, spray paint on your house, or throw a curve with a baseball, you conjure up the same queer law of science that enables an airplane to fly. Daniel Bernoulli, famous Swiss mathematician, discovered and formulated this law more than 200 years ago. Today the "Bernoulli effect" is one of the most important principles of aerodynamics.

Briefly stated, the law is this. Increase the velocity of a fluid (such as air or water) and the pressure inside that fluid is *decreased*!

At first thought it doesn't make sense. Tell Joe Smith that the pressure inside a 60-mile gale is less than the pressure of still air, or that the pressure in the swiftly moving narrows of a river is less than the pressure in its sluggish wider parts, and he'll tell you you're crazy. But there are two kinds of pressure, as Bernoulli explained. The first is *dynamic* pressure, which results when a fluid hits something head on; the second is internal, or *static*, pressure, the pressure of one particle against another within the fluid itself. Dynamic pressure *does* go up with velocity, but in proportion as dynamic pressure goes up, static pressure goes down.

Luckily, this paradox is easier to demonstrate than to explain. For example, suspend two apples (or oranges, or tennis balls) from long strings, so that they hang freely about 1½ inches apart. Then blow smartly between them. What happens? They fly apart? Never! Bernoulli was right. The apples *bump together*. Normal air pressure on the outer sides of the apples pushes them into the region of low pressure created by your swift breath!

To demonstrate again, point an electric fan upward and turn it on. Drop a toy balloon into the air stream. (A paper clip or two

10

What will happen if you blow between these two apples? They'll fly apart, you say?

No! They bump together, pushed by outside air into the vacuum created by your breath.

used as ballast will keep the balloon from being blown too far away.) Although the balloon bobs up and down, it cannot leave the stream because of the envelope of high-speed low-pressure air flowing around it. Every time it reaches the edge of the stream, the quiet, higher pressure air of the atmosphere pushes it back.

An even more mystifying effect is created when you tilt the fan, as shown in the frontispiece. The balloon still stays in the stream, seemingly disobeying the laws of gravity. Only if the fan is tilted so low that the pull of gravity becomes stronger than the upward pressure of the atmosphere does the balloon fall out.

In paint and insecticide sprayers as well as perfume atomizers air at high speed is driven across the upper end of a tube whose lower end dips into the liquid to be sprayed. Since the atmospheric pressure at the bottom of the tube is greater than the pressure of the air speeding over the top, the liquid is forced upward until it is caught in the air stream and hurled along with it.

11

Why Curve Balls Curve

Bernoulli's law also explains why a spinning baseball, a "sliced" golf ball, and a "chopped" tennis ball all deviate from the straight path commonly taken by moving objects.

As a ball whirls, air is carried around with it. On one side of the ball this whirling air is moving *with* the air current produced by the forward motion of the ball; on the other side it is moving *against* the current. The result of such cooperation and opposition is that the air speed along one side of the ball is greater than the air speed along the other. In consequence, the ball curves toward the side past which the air moves fastest.

That this curving is real and its direction predictable from the direction of spin of the ball can be demonstrated at close quarters by means of a ping-pong ball suspended from a string. The string should be about 1 yard long. First draw the ball back, as shown on the next page, and let it go. It swings normally, straight back and forth. Now twist the string about fifty twists to the left, so that the ball will spin clockwise when released. Let it go again. The ball will curve decidedly to your right, tending to turn more and more to the right as it swings. If the string is twisted to the right instead of the left, so that the ball will spin counterclockwise, the ball, when released, will curve to your left.

The complete movement of the ball, after it has been set spinning first in one direction and then the other, is shown in the left-hand photograph on the opposite page. The ball that spins clockwise swings to lower left and upper right. For the ball that spins counterclockwise, the curve of the swing is reversed.

Attempts have been made to prove photographically that baseball curves are not curves at all but are mere optical illusions. It must be remembered, however, that the camera, unless under the most strict scientific control, is also subject to illusions.

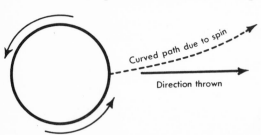

Curved path due to spin

Direction thrown

12

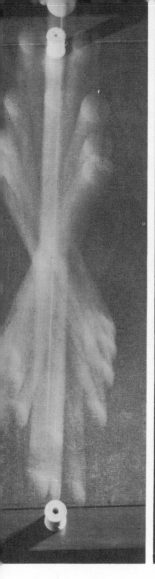

More accurate tests have been performed in which a spinning baseball has been thrown through a series of screens made of fine threads. By measuring the position of the threads broken by the ball in each of the screens, it has been possible to determine the exact location of the ball at a number of points in its travel. These experiments indicate that balls can definitely be made to curve, but that their maximum curve is in the order of 6½ inches. It would be difficult to increase the curve of a baseball beyond this limit because the pitcher's hand can't spin the ball fast enough.

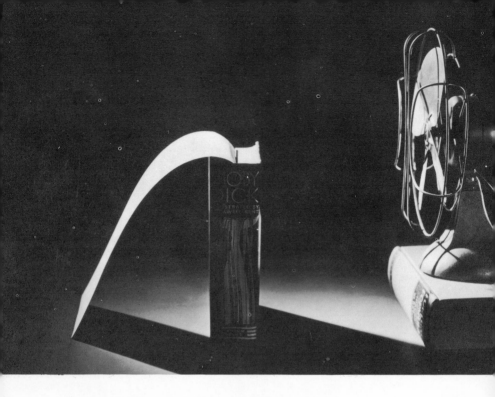

How Does an Airplane Fly?

Incredible as it may seem, the forces discovered by Bernoulli, those selfsame forces that cause paint to rise in a sprayer and baseballs to curve, also enable giant bombers and transport planes to skim through the sky! Popular belief to the contrary, it is the air streaming at breakneck speed over the *top* of an airplane wing that gives it most of its "lift"!

With a strip of paper, a book, and an electric fan you can quickly convince yourself of this fact. Anchor one end of the strip of paper between the leaves of the book, as shown above. For best results curve the windward end of the paper slightly upward (in aeronautical language, give it *camber*), much the same as the upward curve of a real airplane wing.

Now turn on the fan, directing the air current over the top of the paper. Although the book obstructs most of the fan blast beneath the paper, the paper lifts and quickly flutters out straight, as shown in the second photograph. The normal atmospheric pressure below the paper presses the paper upward into the low-pres-

14

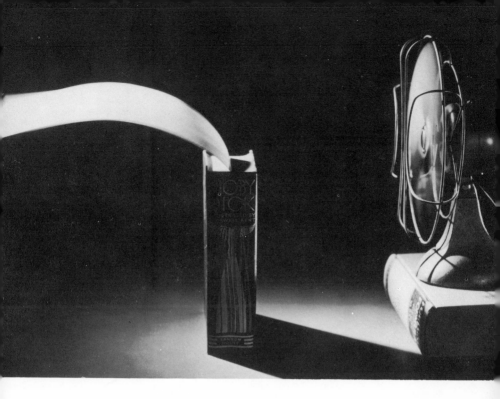

sure, high-velocity air stream above it.

For many years after airplanes were first built and flown, even the men who designed them didn't know exactly what held them in the air. Lift was attributed variously to a positive air pressure on the underside of the wing caused by the forward motion of the plane or to some mysterious suction produced above the wing by air being torn away from it.

Later scientific study of airfoils and airplane models in wind tunnels changed these ideas. Experiments with smoke proved that air was not torn away from the upper surface of a plane wing, as had been supposed, but that it clung closely to the wing surface. Theories had to be revised. It was discovered that the upward curve of the top of the wing surface forced the air to travel more swiftly over the top of the wing than the bottom. The reduced pressure on the upper surface of the wing, produced by this increased velocity, accounted for 75 per cent of the plane's lift. The difference in pressure might be only 2 or 3 ounces to the square inch. But, multiplied by thousands of square inches, this gave a lift in tons.

15

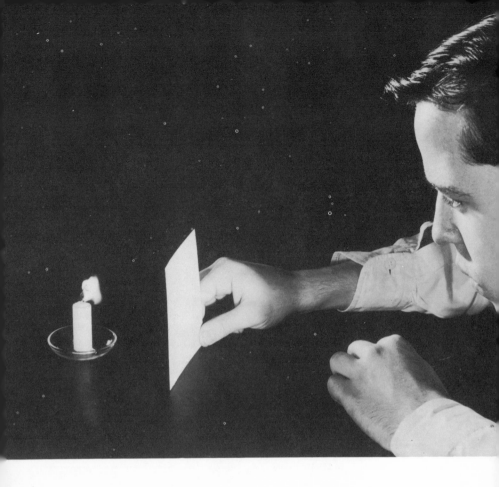

Why Streamlining Is Necessary

To achieve present-day speeds of airplanes, automobiles, trains, and ships, designers took a tip from the sea. Although resistance to movement at slow speeds through air and water is relatively small, resistance to movement at high speeds is tremendous. This resistance could be cut sharply, designers found, if objects were so shaped that air or water flowed smoothly around them. The ideal shape turned out to be that of a blunt-nosed fish—a creature streamlined by Nature a few billion years ago!

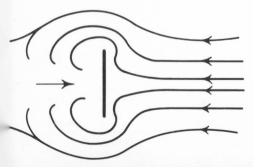

Contrary to popular notion, most fluid resistance is caused not by the air or water that collides with the

16

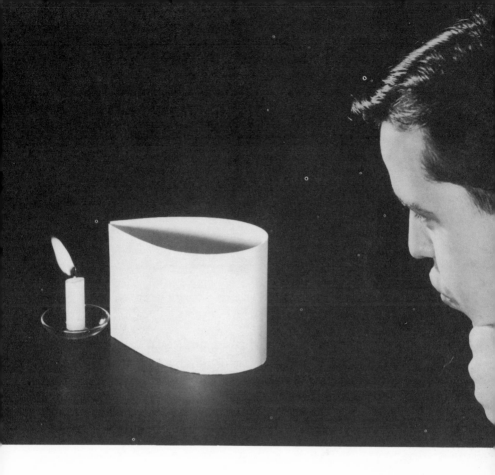

front of a plane or car or ship, but by the air or water that is torn
turbulently off at the *after* end. Do you wish to prove this? Hold a
flat piece of cardboard before a candle flame and blow toward it,
as shown on the opposite page. Instead of streaming away from
you, the flame flutters *at* you! Unable to flow smoothly around the
flat card, the air tumbles erratically past it, creating eddy currents
and a partial vacuum in the rear. It is this disturbance at the rear
that causes most of the "drag" on a plane or speeding car. If you
now substitute a fish-shaped, or so-called "teardrop"-shaped, cardboard for the flat one, as shown
above, and repeat the experiment,
your breath blows the candle steadily from you—almost as if the object were not there!

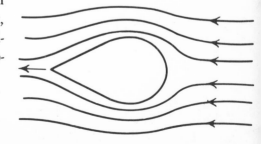

17

Action and Reaction

To every action there is an opposite and equal reaction. So wrote Newton in his famous third law of motion. "If you press a stone with your finger," he continued, "the finger is also pressed by the stone. If a horse draws a stone tied to a rope, the horse will be equally drawn back toward the stone."

If you have ever jumped hastily from the prow of a small boat to the shore, you may have had proof of this law. To propel yourself forward, you had to push backward. Responding to this backward push, the boat ungraciously dropped you overboard!

This two-way nature of force holds true even though one of the objects involved moves so little that it does not seem to move

at all. When you walk, for instance, it is the forward reaction of the ground to the backward push of your feet that enables you to go ahead. For trains to travel over rails, the rails must push forward as hard as the locomotive wheels push backward.

If the rails were not fastened securely to the ground, they would visibly move in reverse. You can demonstrate this with a toy locomotive on a short track. Mount the track on a thin board, as shown above, with round pencils under it as rollers. When you turn on the current, what happens? The track speeds backward as the locomotive goes forward! Although the motion is far too small to worry about, infinitely sensitive instruments might show you that a real locomotive actually rotates the whole earth backward beneath it as it hurtles ahead!

Gun "Kick" Is Due to Reaction

When a cork pops from a bottle, the expanding gases push downward on the bottle with the same force that they hurl the cork into the air. A gun "kicks" back for the same reason. Both obey Newton's third law. Bottle and gun move backward with far less velocity than cork or bullet moves forward because they are much heavier.

With the aid of a bottle and a kitchen scale, you can witness this force of reaction. Put 1 ounce of vinegar into a small soda bottle and add water until the bottle is two-thirds full. Roll up 1 teaspoonful of baking soda in a square of paper napkin and twist the ends. Then put the bottle on the scale, drop the paper cartridge into it, and quickly cork the bottle. Watch the scale. At the instant the cork pops, the scale will be depressed.

By using a large soda bottle, mounting it on round pencils as wheels, and using plain vinegar without extra water, you can make a toy gun, as shown below, which will recoil like a real one.

Whenever a cork pops out of a bottle, gases are pushing downward on the bottle as well as upward on the cork. You can prove it with a scale.

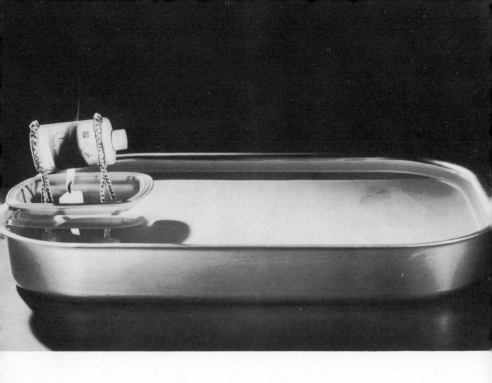

A Toy Ship Explains Rockets and Jets

Today the principle of action and reaction is used spectacularly in military rockets and jet-propelled planes. In both these devices gases shoot out at tremendous speed from nozzles at the after end. In order to move backward, the gases must press forward on the nozzles. It is this reaction force that hurls the rockets and planes through the sky at speeds greater than any previously attained by man.

Although propulsion by reaction is not only the key to jet planes but to the whole new Age of Space, the idea behind it is one of the oldest in mechanics. The very first steam engine in recorded history, the *aeolipile*, or "ball of the wind," invented by Heron of Alexandria probably a century or more before the Christian Era, was jet propelled. In this device, two bent nozzles projected at opposite sides of a hollow sphere which was mounted so that it could rotate on a horizontal axis. Steam issuing swiftly from these nozzles pushed back on them, causing the ball to whirl around much like the head of a rotary lawn sprinkler.

22

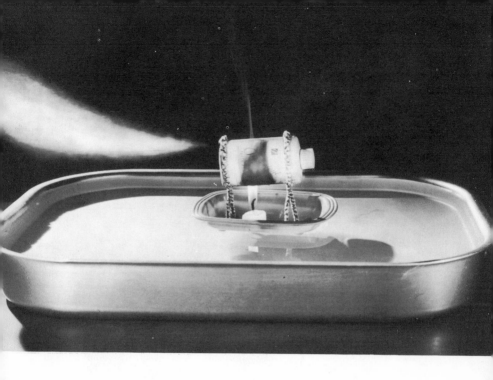

In half a shake, with no materials but a small tooth-powder can, a soap dish, a piece of candle, and four pipe cleaners, you can make a self-propelled toy ship that will demonstrate the principle both of Heron's steam engine and today's jet planes.

Construction is simple. With a needle, just punch a small hole near one edge of the bottom of the tooth-powder can. Mount the can so that it will stand horizontally on pipe-cleaner legs (any kind of wire may be substituted) with the hole at the top. Half fill the can with water and replace the cover. Now place this steam boiler carefully over the lighted candle in the soap-dish boat, which is waiting in a large pan or tub of water.

When the water boils, steam will shoot out the needle-hole "jet." To do so, the steam must also push forward on the boiler. As a result of this push, the boat will speed across the pan!

Contrary to a once-popular notion, the gases from rockets and jet planes do not propel these devices by pushing backward against the air. As far as propulsion is concerned, air is completely unnecessary. That's why we can already send rockets around the earth and the sun and may some day reach out beyond the solar system.

WATER IS WONDERFUL

Weigh Your Friends on a Water Balance

If you stand on a filled syringe-type hot-water bottle, holding the 5-foot tube from it straight up in the air, will your weight force the water out of the end of the tube? If the bottle is of average size and you weigh less than 100 pounds, the answer is "no"—the 2 or 3 ounces of water in the thin tube will balance the weight of your whole body!

By providing the tube with a glass funnel and supporting it as shown, you can use this apparatus to "weigh in" your friends at your next party. Fill the bottle only about half full and lay a small board on top of it to help distribute the weight. It will make balance easier if along each side you also put a block or book slightly thinner than the bottle.

To operate this *hydrostatic balance*, let your friends stand on the bottle while you raise or lower the funnel so that the water level is always visible. Lightweights may raise the water only 3 or 4 feet; heavyweights may cause it to overflow. Oddly enough, if you add water to the funnel the level in the tube will rise only slightly. Instead, the small weight of water will actually lift the person standing on the bottle!

Blaise Pascal, French philosopher and physicist, explained this seeming paradox in 1653. According to "Pascal's law," pressure exerted upon a confined liquid is transmitted in all directions and acts with equal force on all surfaces of equal area. In your balance, the pressure of water at the lower end of the tube is transmitted equally to equal areas all over the inside surface of the bottle. If the area of the tube is 0.05 square inch and the area of the bottle is 50 square inches, then a force exerted at the tube opening is magnified in the bottle to a force a thousand times as great! The same principle is used in the hydraulic press, where small forces may be converted to forces exceeding 10,000 tons.

24

Descartes' Diver Is Still Fascinating

Although today few may recall the religious and scientific works of René Descartes, famous French philosopher, his "Cartesian Diver," or "Bottle Imp," carries on his immortality. For more than 300 years this scientific toy has fascinated grownups as well as youngsters. As a source of instruction, it has found its way into schoolbooks all over the world.

During its three centuries of use, the "Bottle Imp" has changed but little. Generally it takes the form of a small blown-glass imp or devil, which floats on water in a tall jar covered by a rubber diaphragm. When the diaphragm is pressed or released the imp mysteriously dives to the bottom of the jar, rises to the top, or remains poised midway—all in accordance with the operator's will.

With nothing but a tall glass of water and a small vial or bottle you can make an "Imp" that will entertain your friends at the dinner table as well as could the customary manikin. And, because this version is streamlined and free from frills, perhaps your friends can guess how it works merely by close observation.

Invert the unstoppered vial in the water, letting just enough water into it so that it barely floats in the upside-down position. Fill the glass almost to the brim. Then cover the rim of the glass completely with your hand and press your palm into the glass. Curiously, the bottle sinks. Release the pressure, and it rises again. By carefully adjusting the pressure applied by your hand you can make the bottle hesitate in the middle, as shown on the opposite page.

How does it work? Air is easily compressible. Water, on the other hand, can hardly be compressed at all. Pressure on the water, therefore, does not squeeze the water but does squeeze the air remaining in the vial. With more water and less air in it, the vial loses buoyancy and sinks. In the commercial "Cartesian Diver," water enters the little figure through a tiny hole in the foot or, if it's a devil, in the tip of the tail. Submarines, incidentally, dive by letting in water in the same way that the vial does and rise, similarly, by expelling water.

26

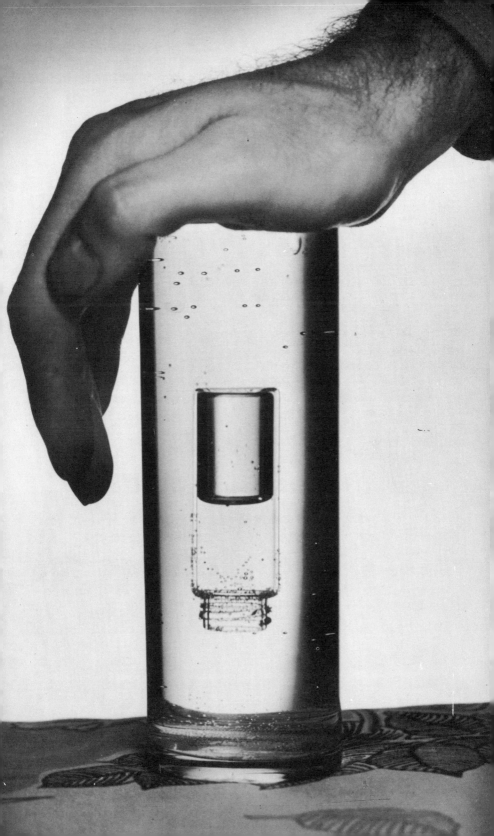

Surface Tension Enables Iron to Float

Although iron window screening is more than seven times as heavy as water, a flat square of it laid carefully on the surface of a body of water will float like a raft. It will even support the additional weight of a large cork, as shown above. If equal care is taken, steel needles and safety-razor blades may also be floated; this is easier when they are slightly oily. Flies, mosquitoes, and other insects can walk on the surface of water without even getting their feet wet.

The reason for such strange phenomena is *surface tension*, the tendency of a liquid surface to act like a stretched elastic membrane. When water comes in contact with air, the molecules at the surface are attracted more strongly to the water beneath than to the air above. The result is that the surface molecules become

more tightly packed together than those in the interior. If an object (such as a fly's foot, window screening, a needle, or a razor blade) is not too heavy and is not easily wet by water, it merely dents this surface layer without breaking through.

Some liquids have greater surface tension than others. Alcohol, for instance, has a considerably lower tension than water. Temperature also affects surface tension. As the thermometer goes up, molecules jump about more freely, and surface tension goes down. That's why hot water leaks more readily through a tiny hole than does cold. Certain substances, such as soap, can lower the surface tension of water considerably.

To prove the last statement convincingly, dip the corner of a bar of soap into the water on which your window-screen raft is floating. The surface film is weakened, and almost instantly the raft sinks to the bottom!

Water Can Be Wetter

If you think water is a synonym for wetness just have a talk with the industrial chemist who knows how often plain water can be perversely "dry." Try to color feathers in water dye, for instance, and the dye rolls merrily off. Spray insecticides on crops and, instead of wetting the leaves uniformly, the solutions collect stubbornly in drops, leaving large leaf areas exposed to insect destruction. Attempt to clean textiles, metals, or glassware with water mixtures, and you are often thwarted by the obstinate refusal of water to wet the dirt.

The reason water resists wetting many things is again due to surface tension. If a surface coming in contact with water has enough attraction for water to break this tension, the surface is wetted. If a surface is oily or otherwise water repellent, however, the water pours off it as off a duck's back.

For centuries men have tried to make water wetter by finding means to lower the surface tension. Ordinary soap was one of the first materials discovered to do this and is still one of the most extensively used. In recent years hundreds of synthetic "wetting agents" have been devised that are far more effective than soap. Many new synthetic detergents and soapless shampoos owe part of their penetrating and cleaning ability to these strange chemicals. A few agents now used in industry are so powerful that 1 part added to 100,000 parts of water will increase the water's wetness by one-third!

To demonstrate how wetting agents work—as well as to convince yourself that they really *do* work—sprinkle a little powdered sulfur on the surface of some water in a tumbler. Although sulfur is heavier than water, it does not sink, because plain water refuses to wet it. Now add a few drops of Drene shampoo or a solution of the detergent Dreft or, better still, one of the wetting materials sold for use in photographic developers, fixers, and toners. Immediately, as in the right-hand tumbler on the opposite page, the wetter water creeps up around the sulfur particles, and they start falling like a miniature snowstorm to the bottom of the glass.

Plain water is "dry" to sulfur floating in the glass at left. A wetting agent added to the water in the other glass causes sulfur to sink.

What Makes the Boat Go?

Toy "mystery boats," which scoot around the bathtub or over the pond without visible means of propulsion, are among the newest playthings that make use of surface tension. The "energy units" of one of these boats consist of pellets of a concentrated wetting agent placed near the stern. As the pellets slowly dissolve, the surface tension of the water directly behind the boat becomes less than that in front. Hence the boat is pulled forward.

With nothing but a piece of cardboard and a chip of soap you can make a little boat that will sail as gallantly as these more elaborate rivals. Cut the cardboard in the shape of a boat, as shown above, and in a little V in its stern insert the bit of soap. Place your boat in a pan of water, and it will move mysteriously about until the whole water surface has been weakened by the soap. The larger the surface of the water, the longer it will sail. If you replenish the water, a stalled boat will start again.

Water Has Spaces between Its Molecules

Would you believe that you can empty the contents of an average-sized salt shaker into a full glass of water without the water's overflowing? With care you can do it, as shown above. Fill the glass to the brim, though don't round it over. Then add the salt very slowly, stirring all the while with a thin wire or a broom straw. This helps dissolve the salt. Although the volume of the water does increase slightly, as can be seen by a heaping-up above the edge, the total volume of solution is not nearly so great as the sum of the individual volumes of salt and water before they were mixed.

Why a solution should have less volume than its component parts is not definitely known. Evidently there are spaces between the molecules of the solvent in which, under favorable conditions, the molecules of the dissolved substance can fit. The amount of shrinkage is erratic and varies with different substances. If you use sugar in place of salt in the present experiment, there will be hardly any volume change at all. On the other hand, a few substances will actually increase the total volume when dissolved.

Osmosis Helps Life Carry On

How nutriment from the food you eat can go right through the walls of your intestines, take a ride in the blood stream, and finally wind up inside any one of the few billion completely enclosed cells of your body, is something to wonder about. The name of the process that makes this possible is *osmosis*. With the help of an uncooked egg and a short glass tube you can soon demonstrate its miraculous action.

Carefully break away a patch of shell from one end of the egg without puncturing the white membrane underneath. Break a smaller hole through both shell and membrane in the other end and over this attach the tube with sealing wax. Then stand the bottom of the egg in a glass of water, so that the exposed membrane is submerged.

Although the contents of the egg are separated from the water by the membrane, the water will find its way through. Leave the egg for half an hour, then take a look. The insides of the egg are rising slowly in the tube. If left long enough, the contents may even overflow.

What's the reason? The egg membrane—membrane much the same as that of the cell walls in your body—contains minute pores through which tiny water molecules and the molecules of certain dissolved substances can pass rather freely, but through which the big molecules of egg albumen or cell protoplasm cannot pass at all. By a similar provision, food and water can get into your body cells and wastes can get out, but the life-giving protoplasm can't escape!

In the egg, water passes both ways through the membrane, but because the pores on the inside are partially obstructed by the albumen, more water enters than leaves. Hence the egg is slowly crowded from its shell.

Osmosis occurs wherever two liquids containing different concentrations of dissolved matter are separated by a semipermeable membrane. The movement of fluid is from the weaker to the more concentrated solution. Plants and trees extract their water and food from the soil by means of this same wonderful process.

Osmosis Conjures Up a Magic Garden

A colorful chemical garden in which some of the "plants" grow before your eyes affords a beautiful demonstration of a more complex form of osmotic action. You can buy complete kits to make such gardens, but if you have access to a chemical supply house or toy chemistry set a homemade one may be even better.

Sprinkle about ¼ inch of coarse sand on the bottom of a small fish globe or a low jar that will hold about a quart. Now almost fill the remainder of the globe or jar with sodium silicate solution (water glass) diluted with an equal amount of water.

"Seeds" for your garden consist of such salts as copper sulfate, ferrous sulfate, zinc sulfate (which may be obtained at the local drugstore), nickel sulfate, cobalt chloride, and manganese chloride. If you can't get them all, use what you can. For best results, crystals should be at least ⅛ inch in diameter. All are of different colors and should be dropped to the bottom so that the colors will be distributed attractively.

Within a matter of seconds, some of these crystals will be sending up shoots; in minutes a few may reach the top of the solution; while, in an hour or two, the garden should be completely grown— a forest of intricate and varicolored growth which suggests some undersea fairyland.

After a day, carefully siphon off the sodium silicate solution and replace with fresh water. Because the crystals of metallic silicates which make them up are insoluble, the plants should last until they are broken by jarring.

HEAT, COLD, AND THE WEATHER

Black Makes the Best Heat Radiator

Do black pots hold heat longer than light, shiny ones? Does the color of its paint alter the heat-giving ability of a radiator? Does the color of clothes affect their warmness or coolness?

You may help settle all these questions by means of an easy experiment. Take an empty tin can and smoke half of it, inside and out, over a candle flame. Then suspend a 100-watt light bulb in the can so that it hangs as near the center as possible. If you now cup your hands around the blackened and shiny sides of the can, as shown at right, you discover that the black side radiates considerably more heat than does the bright side!

If you couple dullness with darkness and shininess with lightness, you will find that the result of this test is universally true; objects with dull, dark surfaces are the best absorbers and radiators of both light and heat; objects with shiny, light surfaces *reflect* light and heat well but absorb and radiate it poorly.

As a consequence, dull, black pots heat fast and cool fast. Although shiny ones take longer to heat, they also hold their heat longer after the source of heat has been removed. Tests prove that radiators give out from 5 to 10 per cent more radiant heat when coated with ordinary linseed-oil paint than they do when coated with aluminum or other "bronze" paints, the bright surface of the latter reflecting back part of the heat. On the other hand, roofs coated with light-colored or bright metallic paint help keep houses cooler by bouncing back instead of absorbing rays from the sun.

Similarly, light-colored clothes help protect you from the direct rays of the sun in summer. Dark clothes, by absorbing these rays, help keep you warm in winter. On dull days, in the shade, or indoors, however, the effect of lightness or darkness is chiefly psychological. Under such conditions weave, kind, and weight of material are more important than color.

38

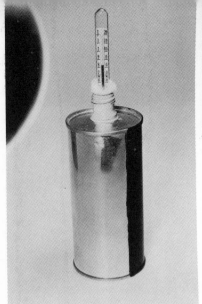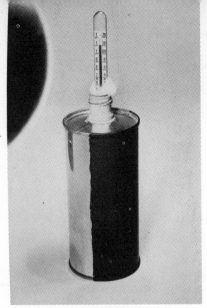

Absorption Controls Heat in Space Ships

Instrument compartments in satellites and other space vehicles are kept within common earth temperatures by the clever application of this knowledge of absorption and reflection. Unmodified, the polished metal shell of a space ship would bounce back so much heat from the sun that the instruments inside would freeze. If completely blackened, it would absorb so much heat that inside parts might melt or scorch. By attaching to the polished shell a small patch of black material (often provided with a mechanism for varying its size with changes of exposure to sunlight), the temperature can be held within a range best suited to the telemetering devices that collect data and send it back to earth.

You can demonstrate dramatically how this control works with the help of the apparatus shown above. Choose a narrow-neck can with a paper label; remove the label, and paint half the can a flat black. Insert a thermometer midway in the can and hold it with cotton stuffed around it in the neck. Now place the can in sunlight or in front of a reflector-spot bulb. By turning the can so that different proportions of black and polished surface face the light, the temperature inside can be kept at any desired degree—from a few degrees to, say, seventy degrees above that outside!

Power from the Sun

Batteries to operate the instruments of earth satellites and space probes get their power free from the vast energy of sunlight. This energy is also used to purify water, run engines, heat homes, and to cook food in communities where fuel is scarce.

You can harness a little of this free energy with the simple fly-power motor shown in operation above. Make it from the everyday items pictured below. Cut out the bottom of the can and paint the can black. For legs, clip the clothespins to the lower edge, and, for a pivot fasten a sewing needle upright to the neck with two rubber bands, letting the point project an inch above the top. For the rotor, make eight L-shaped cuts in the bottom of a cupcake cup, and bend each up slightly to serve as a windmill blade. Finally, balance the cup carefully on the point of the needle. To avoid external drafts, set up your motor inside a sunny window or under a reflector lamp. Light absorbed by the can heats the air within. This rises through the neck and pushes on the blades in the cup, causing the cup to spin.

41

A Calling-card Kettle

Maybe your friends will smile when you turn up the edges of a calling card, pour water into the tray that results, and propose to boil the water by the heat of a match or two. But don't worry. The water will boil readily. And, what's more, the bottom of the card will no more than get smoked as long as any water remains.

The reason? First of all, water can't normally be heated above its boiling point, which in open air at sea level is 212 degrees Fahrenheit or 100 degrees centigrade. After this point has been reached, all further heat that is applied to it is utilized in changing the water to steam. As your water cools the card to its own temperature and as it can never reach the kindling temperature of the paper, the card just can't burn.

This perverseness of water explains why you can't boil potatoes faster by turning up the gas. A small flame, just high enough to keep the water boiling continuously, will cook food fully as rapidly as the biggest flame available—and with an obvious saving in money and fuel.

Can You Raise This Ice Cube?

Float an ice cube in a cup or tumbler full of water and challenge a dinner guest to remove the cube with the help of a short piece of string. For assistance, he must use only items normally found on the dinner table. No tactics so crude as tying the string around the cube or using a spoon as a helper are permissible. When he gives up, merely lay the end of the string, well wet, across the top of the cube and sprinkle a little salt along each side of the string. The salt lowers the freezing point of the ice that it touches, causing it to melt (just as it causes ice to melt on the sidewalk). In melting, the salted ice robs heat from the adjacent ice and the water on the string. Within a matter of seconds, the string is frozen fast enough for you to lift the cube!

Moisture May Be Squeezed from the Air

In squeezing water from humid air, air-conditioning experts use the same principle that Nature uses in squeezing rain from the clouds. Both lower the temperature of the air to below what is known as the "dew point." As a result, the excess moisture automatically falls out.

To understand how this works try to imagine air as a sort of gaseous sponge whose capacity to hold moisture increases as the temperature goes up and decreases as it goes down. At 80 degrees Fahrenheit, for example, each cubic foot of air can contain nearly 11 grains of water vapor; at 50 degrees it can hold 4 grains; while at 16 degrees it can hold only 1 grain. If, then, air that is saturated with moisture at 80 degrees is cooled to 50 degrees, 7 grains of moisture will be wrung out of each cubic foot.

The sweat on cold-water pipes, cellar walls, and a tumbler of ice water in hot summer weather is in every case caused by this squeezing of water from the atmosphere by lowering the temperature. Dew on the ground is similarly formed by the condensation of moisture on grass and other cooled objects near the earth.

Because of this variable capacity of the air for holding moisture, we can calculate the relative amount of moisture in the air, or the *relative humidity*, simply by determining the temperature at which moisture begins to condense from it, its dew point.

Half fill a tumbler with water at room temperature and slowly add cracked ice while stirring with a thermometer. Note the temperature at which moisture first becomes visible on the glass. Stop adding ice and then note the temperature at which the moisture disappears. The dew point is the average of these two figures.

If you know the dew point, it is easy to determine the relative humidity. Refer to the table on page 45 and divide the moisture capacity of the air at the dew point by the capacity of the air at room temperature. If the room temperature, for instance, is 70 degrees (vapor capacity, 7.99 grains) and the dew point is 50 degrees (vapor capacity, 4.09 grains), the air is 4.09/7.99, or 51.2 per cent saturated.

MOISTURE CAPACITY OF AIR	
Temp. °F.	Grains per Cu. Ft.
40	2.86
50	4.09
60	5.76
70	7.99
80	10.95

By first finding the temperature at which moisture condenses on a glass of water, you can easily determine the relative humidity of the air around you. Just divide the moisture capacity of the air at this "dew point" by its capacity at room temperature. The table above will give you the figures you need.

Relative Humidity Affects Comfort

When we complain about the "humidity," we generally refer to the high relative humidity often suffered in warm weather. When air is hot and damp, perspiration clings to us, ink and paint refuse to dry, foods become moldy, and walls mildewed. Although we can't do much about the outside humidity, we can reduce the indoor humidity with such drying agents as calcium chloride or silica gel or by squeezing out moisture with a cooling system.

For the sake of health and comfort, however, it is also important to *add* moisture to warm indoor air in winter. For cold outdoor air, even when saturated, becomes drier than the air over the Sahara when brought indoors and heated to 70 or 80 degrees. This desert-dry air causes the mucous membranes of the eyes, nose, and throat to dry out and become more susceptible to infection. Because perspiration evaporates faster, we feel chilly at higher temperatures. Merely by adding moisture to the air until the relative humidity reaches 45 or 50 per cent, we can make a temperature of 65 degrees feel as comfortable as one of 80 at low humidity!

Because the rate of evaporation (and hence the cooling effect) of water at any given temperature depends upon the degree of moisture saturation of the air at that temperature, the relative humidity can be determined by comparing the reading of a thermometer whose bulb is dry with another whose bulb is wet. Mount two thermometers as shown at right. Wrap a piece of absorbent

Dry-bulb temp. (deg. F.)	Difference between dry and wet bulbs (deg. F.)					
	3	6	9	12	15	18
	Relative humidity (per cent)					
65	85	70	56	44	31	20
70	86	72	60	48	36	26
75	87	74	62	51	40	31
80	87	75	64	54	44	35

cloth tightly around the bulb of one and let the lower end dip into a small bottle of water. When the cloth is wet, fan the air about the thermometers for several minutes. Then note the reading of both. Find the relative humidity by referring to the table at left.

Water Does Not Heat Until Ice Melts

After you have cooled your iced tea to the freezing point with a generous supply of ice cubes, do you imagine you have to keep adding cubes in order to maintain the same low temperature? Theoretically, you don't have to add another cube as long as you keep stirring and even a fraction of a cube remains!

If you don't believe this, why not convince yourself by performing a simple test which, on the face of it, is even less credible? Put some ice cubes and water into a small pot or the bottom section of a vacuum coffee maker and stir with a thermometer until the temperature goes down to 32 degrees Fahrenheit, the freezing point of water. Now place the pot on an electric grill or over a low gas flame, as shown at right. Stir constantly as you watch the thermometer. If you do a good job of stirring, the temperature will not rise a degree as long as a bit of ice is left!

The reason for this surprising phenomenon can be found in the conditions that govern the freezing of water and the melting of ice. To freeze water we have to do far more than lower its temperature to the freezing point. From every gram of water that changes into ice, 80 calories of heat must be removed. That is why large bodies of water give off considerable heat and keep the air around them comparatively warm while they are freezing.

To melt ice, conversely, we must add just as much heat to it as was removed in freezing. In other words, to change each gram of ice to water of exactly the same temperature, we must supply 80 calories of heat, or enough heat to raise 1 gram of water at room temperature to the boiling point. As long as any ice remains in water at freezing temperature, whatever heat is applied must first melt the ice completely before it can start to raise the temperature of the water.

It is because of the large amount of heat needed to melt ice that ice is so effective in the refrigerator to keep things cold. As it melts, it extracts heat from the foodstuffs, without itself becoming warmer. The practice of blanketing ice to make it last longer obviously reduces its value as a refrigerant.

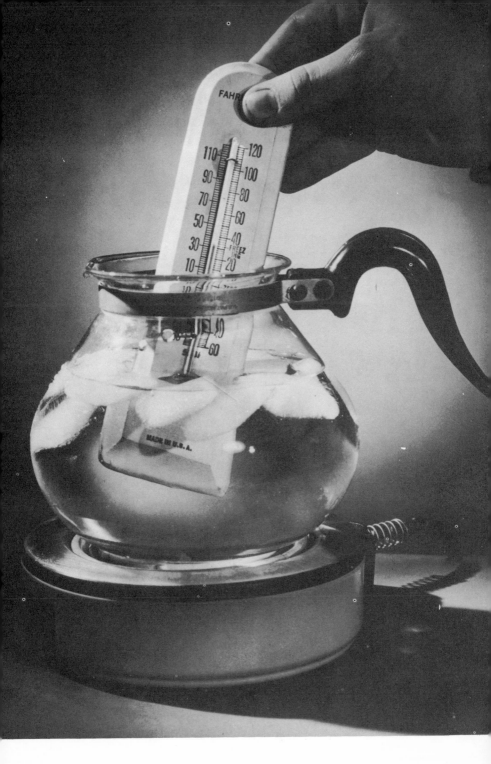

Freezing without Ice

One of the latest gadgets designed to cool a bottled beverage merely consists of a container in which you stand the bottle, plus a mysterious powder that you dissolve in water. As soon as the powder dissolves, the water becomes ice cold and chills the bottle. It's an expensive method but handy in an emergency.

To show how it works, just stir some photographer's "hypo" in water. If the water is cold enough to begin with, you can cool it enough more to freeze a tumbler to a cork coaster or a block of wood! Half fill a thin-bottomed tumbler with cold water, smear a few drops of water on the coaster, then set the glass on it. Now add an equal amount of hypo to the water in the glass and stir until dissolved. By this time the glass should be frozen to the coaster, as shown at right.

Ammonium nitrate will lower the temperature even more than hypo. Many other salts produce a similar effect. When they dissolve, their molecules are given greater freedom, just as when ice melts. To get this freedom, they absorb heat energy from their surroundings. If a solid produces *heat* when it dissolves, this is due to a chemical reaction that gives off more heat than is absorbed.

Why Winds Whirl

What makes hurricanes and tornadoes spin? Why do ocean currents, projectiles, and all the long-range winds of the earth invariably veer from a straight path?

Gaspard Gustave de Coriolis, a French mathematician, discovered the answer more than a century and a quarter ago. The northern and southern hemispheres of the earth act like two giant turntables that whirl in opposite directions. At their rims, the equator, they travel at a rate of about a thousand miles an hour; at their poles, they are virtually stationary.

Send a wind, or any other free-moving object, across the surface of either of these hemisphere-turntables and it not only travels forward but moves sideways at a velocity given it by the earth's spin at the point from which it started. If it travels from a faster-spinning part of the earth to a slower-spinning part, the wind or object gets ahead of the earth beneath it; if it travels from a slower-spinning part to one that spins faster, it lags behind. The result is a curved path of travel—to the right in the northern hemisphere, and to the left in the southern.

Because of this *Coriolis force*, all long-distance winds and sea currents deviate from a straight course; masses of air end up by whirling around areas of high and low pressure instead of going directly from one to the other; long-range missiles must be aimed many miles to one side in order to pinpoint their mark.

You can demonstrate the Coriolis force with the setup above. Punch a tiny hole about an inch from the bottom of a small can;

fill the can with water, and place it on a cake pan. You may then either rotate the pan alone or on a Lazy Susan, as shown. When the pan is still, the water squirts straight out from the hole. But turn it counterclockwise, to represent the eastward rotation of the earth as seen from above the North Pole, and the stream curves to the right, as shown in the second photo. Place the can in the center of the pan with the stream heading toward the rim, turn again, and the stream again bends toward the right.

Although the direction of rotation of all hurricanes and nearly all tornadoes is governed by the Coriolis force, that of local storms, "whirlwinds," and the spin of water down the drain is not.

You can easily simulate a miniature "tornado," and also disprove the legend of the drainpipe spin. Fill a funnel by pouring in water at an angle so an initial spin is created in one direction or the other. The water will continue to spin in that direction until the funnel is empty. Fill it so there is no initial rotation and the water will run out quietly without turning either way.

PROBLEMS OF GRAVITY

Why the Leaning Tower Doesn't Fall

As treated here, the famous Leaning Tower of Pisa is just a symbol of everything and everybody that seems in danger of toppling over. The two-decker Fifth Avenue and London busses, a mountainous load of hay, the Empire State Building in a high wind, your car skidding on two wheels around a curve, a tottering friend—all these things pose the same problem. In terms of science, just how far can such precarious-seeming objects lean before they overturn completely?

The answer is simple: An object can lean without falling as long as a straight line leading from its center of gravity to the center of the earth passes through the object's base.

This *center of gravity* is an imaginary point at which we can consider the entire weight of an object to be concentrated. You can easily locate it on any plane object by the method shown in the upper left-hand photograph on the next page. Merely suspend the object (here a cut-out representation of the tower of Pisa) successively from two or more points (say A, B, and C). Hang a weighted thread from the point of suspension and draw a line behind the thread as the object hangs from each point. The X where the lines intersect marks the center of gravity.

If you now suspend your weight-on-the-thread so that it hangs freely from the center-of-gravity point and lean your tower against a wall while its base stands on the edge of a book, you can find out for yourself just how far over it can go without falling. As long as the line remains within the base line of the tower, as shown at upper right, the tower keeps its footing. The instant the line passes outside, down she tumbles!

The lower the center of gravity, the farther over an object can lean. Thus, by concentrating the weight of buildings, cars, and boats as low as possible, designers make them more stable.

54

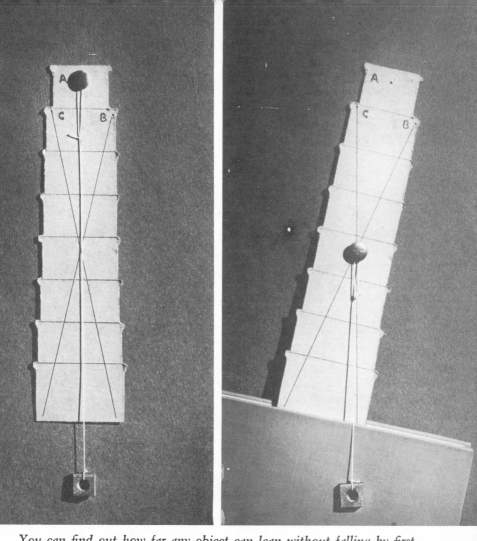

You can find out how far any object can lean without falling by first finding (above left) its center of gravity, or the point at which it balances perfectly (below). The object will not fall as long as a plumb line dropped from this center passes inside the base (above right).

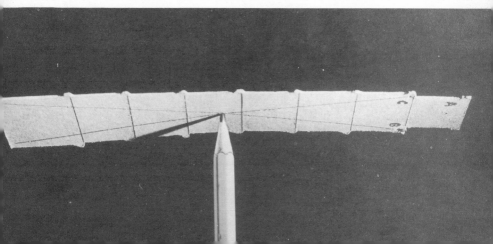

A Low Center of Gravity Gives Stability

By weighting objects so that their center of gravity lies *below* the point of support, you can conjure up an endless array of balancing feats that have been the stock in trade of toymakers and dinner-table scientists for centuries.

It is an easy matter, for instance, to balance a cup, two dinner knives, and a strip of newspaper on the tip of your index finger. Challenge anyone to do this at your next dinner party. When all the guests have failed, show them how it's done.

Cross the two knives (the heavier the handles, the better) through the handle of the cup, and hold them by means of the rolled newspaper. In this position, the heavy knife handles lower the center of gravity of the setup to a point below the tip of your finger. The cup is so stable that it can be balanced even when partly filled with coffee!

Another paradox of the same sort requires a carpenter's 2-foot folding rule. If you hold one end of the rule—hinge side down—on the edge of a table, the outer section naturally drops. Can you make this limp end stand out *by hanging a hammer on it*? It seems impossible, but it can be done, as shown below. The hammer not only holds up the end of the rule but balances the whole rule on the edge of the table! The loop of string causes the hammer to act as a lever that pushes up on the end of the rule, and the heavy hammer head puts the center of gravity beneath the table.

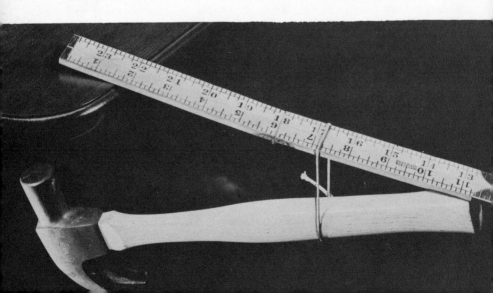

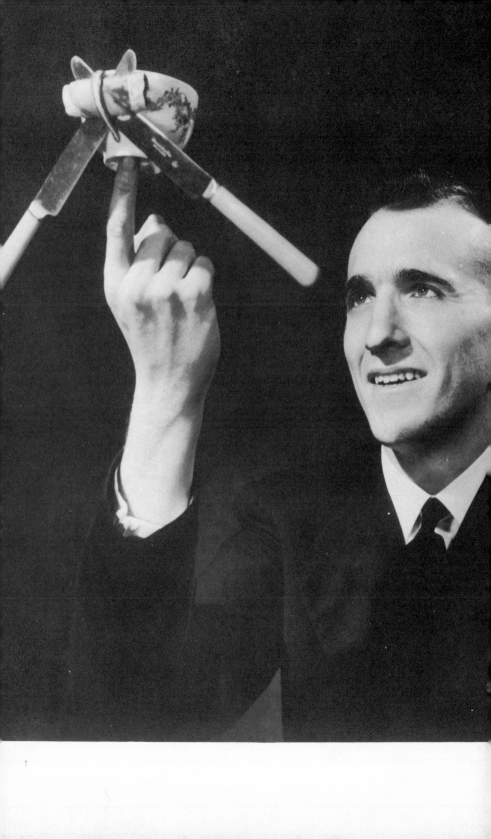

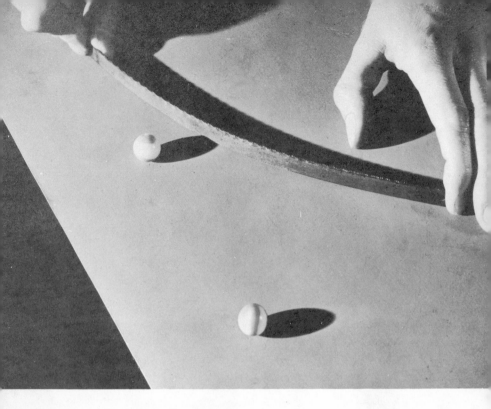

Which Will Reach the Ground First?

Though it may seem hard to believe, a bullet shot horizontally from a gun over level ground will reach the earth at the same time as a similar bullet dropped to the ground from the level of the muzzle of the gun.

You can prove this—in principle at least—with two marbles and a hacksaw blade set up near the edge of a table as shown above. If you release the near end of the blade, the marbles shoot off the table. Although one marble is thrown much farther than the other, the simultaneous click of their fall tells you that they both reach the floor at once.

The reason? All bodies, neglecting air resistance, fall toward the earth at the same rate. The fact that a falling object may also be traveling horizontally has no influence whatever on the speed of its vertical descent. Any bullet can travel only so far as its velocity can take it before the constant acceleration of gravity has pulled it to the ground.

58

A Problem of Balance

If you weight one end of a curtain rod with wire, will it be easier to balance the rod vertically on the tip of your finger when the weighted end is on the top or on the bottom? If you say "bottom," you're wrong! The base of the rod is so small and your finger so unsteady that the rod will try to fall whether the center of gravity is high or low. When it is high, however, the rod takes longer to topple; hence you have more time to check the fall.

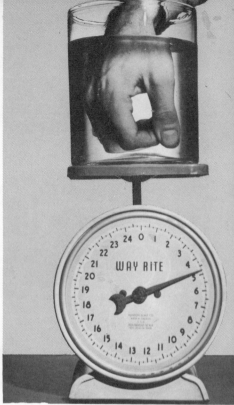

Page Mr. Archimedes!

If you stick your hand into a jar of water without touching the sides or bottom of the jar, will the jar of water be heavier? If you think it will, can you guess how much and give a logical explanation for your answer?

Put such a jar of water on a scale and check your answer by experiment. Odd as it may seem, the jar of water does weigh more when you immerse your hand in it. What determines the amount? If you mark the height of the water in the jar with your hand in it, then remove your hand and refill the jar to that mark, you will find out. The jar will now weigh exactly what it did when your hand was there.

Archimedes explained this phenomenon more than 2,000 years ago. When an object is immersed in a container of water, not touching the bottom, the weight it adds to the container is equal to the weight of the water displaced by it.

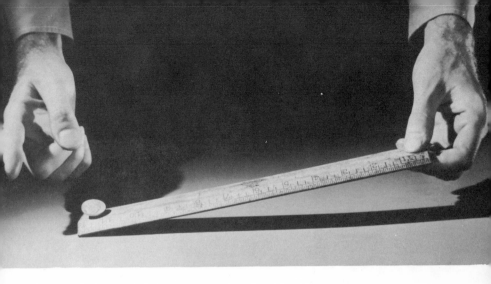

Faster Than Gravity!

Here's a paradox of physics that even your scientifically minded friends may not be able to explain. Ordinarily, no object can fall faster than the normal acceleration of gravity. Yet here is something that evidently *does*.

Place a coin near one end of a ruler or other flat stick, and hold the ruler near both ends, so that it is parallel with a table and several inches above it. Now release the end of the ruler holding the coin and let the end drop freely. Even if your eye is not quick enough to see it, a distinct click tells you that the ruler reaches the table before the coin!

The reason? Simply that the end of the ruler actually does fall faster than the coin! When supported at one end, a falling stick acts as a compound pendulum, whose center of percussion (a point one-third of the way from the free end) falls with the acceleration of gravity. Parts nearer the free end fall faster; parts toward the supported end, more slowly. You can prove this by moving the coin to different parts of the ruler and dropping as before. When the coin is nearer the free end than the center of percussion, you hear a click as it hits the ruler. (Don't confuse with clicks due to bouncing.) When at this center, there is no click. When nearer the supported end, the coin wants to go faster than the ruler but can't.

The Pendulum Keeps Time

The steady swing of a pendulum has helped keep time for almost 300 years. That the beat of any pendulum is absolutely constant was first noticed by Galileo, when the scientist was a youth of nineteen. The story has it that in 1583, while praying in the cathedral at Pisa, his attention was caught by the movement of a great lamp which had been left swinging after it had been lighted. Galileo began to time its oscillations by the beat of his own pulse. To his astonishment, the time taken for the lamp to make each swing was precisely the same at the moment it began as at the moment before it stopped.

Experiments made later proved to him that the time of a pendulum's swing has nothing to do with its weight or material but is proportional to the square root of its length. In 1641, after he had become blind, Galileo dictated to his son a description and drawing of the first pendulum clock.

The split-second timing of the pendulum is due to the constant acceleration given it by gravity. Within limits, the length of the swing, or amplitude, doesn't alter this timing. You can learn the principles with a marble tied to a string. Make the length 39 inches, and your pendulum will swing from one side to the other in almost exactly 1 second. According to Galileo's rule, a pendulum that would make a swing in 2 seconds would have to be *four times* as long; while one that would make the swing in ½ second would be only *one-fourth* as long.

62

Why a Baseball Bat Stings

Every time you take a sound swat at a baseball, you apply correctly an important law of physics; every time you split a bat or the bat stings your hands, you disobey this law. For baseball bats swing, hit, and tremble according to the rules of the pendulum.

Unlike the *simple pendulum* described on the preceding page, your bat is a *compound pendulum*—a pendulum that acts as if it were a series of simple pendulums strung end to end. If you pivot it between two fingers at the point where it is usually gripped and set it to swinging, the bat pendulum will keep time with a marble pendulum shorter than itself.

The point on the bat opposite the marble —when they are swinging in step—is called its *center of oscillation*. It is also the bat's *center of percussion*. Strike the bat at this point with a hammer, stick, or ball, and you feel no vibration. Strike it anywhere else and, due to its inability to oscillate uniformly, the bat shudders, stings your hand, and perhaps cracks.

If a baseball bat were uniformly thick, its center of percussion would be two-thirds of the distance from the grip end. Because it tapers, the center is nearer the striking end.

This same law applies to machinery and to hand tools such as hammers and axes. For instance, if an ax handle is too long, the center of percussion may be in the handle instead of the head. Such an ax shudders, and the handle may break.

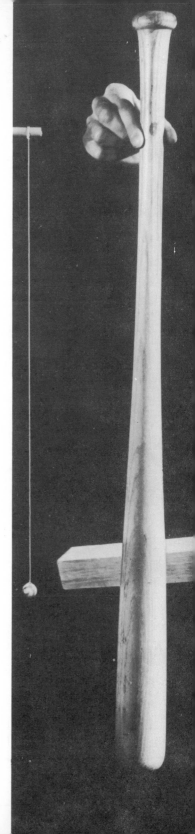

FORCES AND INERTIA

Inertia Is a Universal Property of Matter

Whenever an object is at rest, it will stay that way until some external force moves it. Once started, it will keep moving straight ahead and at the same velocity until an opposing force turns up to stop it. The more matter the object contains (the greater its *mass*), the more force is needed either to start it from rest or to stop it after it has gotten going.

Significantly, Newton called this unwillingness of matter to change its motion *inertia*, or "laziness." It is the one attribute of matter that is constant throughout the universe and can't be tampered with by man. Although a pound of cheese would weigh much less on the moon and nothing at all at the center of the earth, its inertia would be exactly the same at either place as it is here.

It is because of inertia that a train chugs with all its might to get started. Inertia, too, causes the train to keep plunging ahead long after the brakes have been applied for an emergency. When your car runs into a tree, inertia unfortunately insists that *you* keep going. Inertia tightens the head of a hammer when you thump the end of the handle on a bench. It explains the circus strong-man act in which a modern Hercules sustains the blows of a sledge hammer on a heavy slab of concrete held upon his chest; instead of adding to his woes the block, with its inertia, forms a better cushion than a feather pillow!

To demonstrate the principle of inertia, suspend a heavy book from a string and tie a similar string below it. Apply this principle, and you can now break either string at will, just by pulling on the bottom string! Here's how. To break the top string, pull steadily downward on the lower one; the top string gets the force of your pull plus the weight of the book. To break the lower one, just give it a quick jerk. Inertia prevents the full impact of a short, sharp pull from reaching the upper string.

64

If our friend brings his hands together, which way will the stick fall?

Friction Varies with Pressure

Hold a yardstick or a foot rule across your extended index fingers, letting one end protrude much farther than the other. If you now draw your fingers slowly together, which way do you think the stick will fall? Most people will say at the protruding end. Just to be contrary, a few will bet on the other. Actually, the stick won't fall either way. It will wind up balanced on your two fingers, which always meet in the middle!

It's all a matter of weight governing friction. The amount each finger can slide under the stick depends upon the proportion of the stick's weight that bears down upon it. As the finger nearest the center always supports the greater proportion of the weight, this finger cannot slide until the other finger has come equally near the center. Then both fingers can slide uniformly toward each other, finally meeting in the middle. If one finger is placed directly under the center of the stick, this finger cannot slide at all.

66

You're wrong! It won't fall either way but will always end up like this!

Friction, the force that resists the sliding of one body over another, is caused chiefly by the interlocking of minute hills and dales that are present even on the smoothest surfaces. With any two given surfaces, friction is proportional to the force that presses the surfaces together. Oddly enough, the area of contact makes little difference.

The effects of friction are both bad and good. In your automobile and in all kinds of machinery, friction wastes energy by turning it into useless heat. It also wears away the parts that slide over each other. On the other hand, without friction between your tires and the road your car couldn't move; without friction between your feet and the ground you couldn't walk; mountains would slide into valleys; textiles would fall apart; you couldn't build a house by present-day methods because nails, screws, nuts, and bolts wouldn't hold. One of the problems of science, therefore, is to try to find means to increase friction where necessary and to reduce it where wasteful.

Make a Spool Roll Either Way

This puzzling stunt is performed with the help of an empty typewriter or adhesive-tape spool around which has been wound a yard of ribbon or paper tape. Merely by pulling the end of the ribbon, as shown, you can make the spool roll toward you, away from you, or just drag along without rolling at all!

How is this done? It's all a matter of pulling the ribbon so that the line of pull cuts the table either to one side or the other of the point of contact of the spool with the table or intersecting this point, as shown in the diagram below. Leverage does the work, with the point of contact of the spool with the table as the fulcrum. You can figure it out for yourself by studying the drawings.

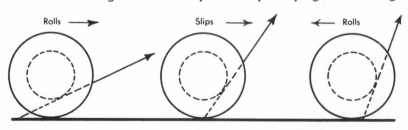

Which Egg Is Boiled?

Merely by spinning an egg, you can tell whether it is hard-boiled or raw. On saucers, briskly spin a boiled egg and a raw egg and note the way each spins. The hard-boiled egg spins long and steadily; it may even try to stand on end. The raw egg spins reluctantly, wobbles, and soon stops. Now spin them again, this time stopping each egg with your hand in the midst of its spinning. Curiously, the boiled egg remains still when you release it, while the raw one starts spinning again of its own accord!

The reason for this strange action on the part of the raw egg is internal friction. The initial motion of the shell is so rapid that the inner layers of semiliquid substance slip on the outer layers and change part of the energy of rotation into heat. Hence the egg cannot spin for long. But, when the shell is stopped, the liquid interior continues to revolve. This starts the shell spinning again when it is released.

Practical use of liquid friction is made in the mariner's compass, where the compass card is mounted in a bowl containing alcohol and water. By resisting small, quick turns of the card the liquid helps smooth out troublesome vibrations.

How Cars and Boats Ride on Air

Cars without wheels that skim over roadless fields, and boats that glide over rivers and bays at airplane speeds without ever touching the water are the newest and most fantastic developments in surface transportation. Although individual designs differ, all depend for their almost frictionless motion upon a cushion of air between the bottom of the vehicle and the earth or water.

With nothing but a 6-inch metal piepan for a car, a small empty spool for a coupling, and a 5-cent balloon as a source of compressed air, you can quickly build a model that will demonstrate in action how such air-supported vehicles work.

Choose a pan with a smooth flat bottom, invert it, and in the center punch or drill a hole from about $\frac{1}{32}$ to $\frac{1}{16}$ inch in diameter (the larger the hole, the easier it will be to inflate the balloon, but the faster the air will leak out during operation). With quick-drying cement, fasten one end of the spool to the inside of the piepan, centering it over the hole in the pan. After the cement has dried, roll back the neck of the balloon as far as possible (to prevent the balloon from swaying when the car is moving, and so throwing the car off course), then stretch the neck over the spool and unroll part of it, as shown at right below.

To operate the device, first inflate the balloon by blowing through pursed lips pressed tightly around the hole in the bottom of the pan. Then place the pan on a smooth table top or linoleum floor and give it a slight push. Instead of scraping along for a mere few inches, as the piepan alone would have done, your model car—cushioned on a thin film of air flowing between pan and surface—skims frictionlessly right across the table or to the other side of the room!

Centrifugal Force May Fool You!

If you have ever whirled a ball tied to the end of a string in a circle, you have felt the outward pull of the ball on your hand. If you have turned a sharp curve in a car going at high speed, you have felt yourself being pressed against the outward side of the seat. In both these experiences you have gotten the feeling that there must be some *centrifugal*, or "center-fleeing," force that tries to hurl all whirling bodies straight out into space.

That, scientifically speaking, there is no such force is hard to believe. Cut the string of the whirling ball, however, and you can prove it; instead of flying outward from the center, the ball shoots off in a straight line tangent to the circle! If the side of the car seat should break, you would find yourself, not being hurled outward, but moving straight forward in the direction toward which you were going at the time the seat broke!

What, then, produces the effect so commonly observed? According to Newton's first law of motion every moving body continues in a straight line unless compelled to do otherwise by some outside urge. To make a body travel in a circle, you must actually push it or pull it toward the center of the circle. So-called "centrifugal" force is the effect produced by the resistance of the body to this pulling or pushing. It is the equal and opposite *reaction* to the *centripetal*, or "center-seeking," force that is directing the body *toward the center!* Remove this centripetal force, and the centrifugal force instantly disappears!

In the case of the circling ball, the string supplies the centripetal force. In the case of the turning car, the friction of the tires on the road furnishes it. If this friction is not great enough, the efforts of the car to travel in a straight line cause it to skid. Sharp curves on highways and railroads are tilted inward, or "banked," to supply extra centripetal force. The heavier the car and the faster it is traveling, the steeper the road must be banked to keep it from skidding.

With a paper plate which has been cut in two and a marble you can demonstrate how centripetal force works. Arrange the sections

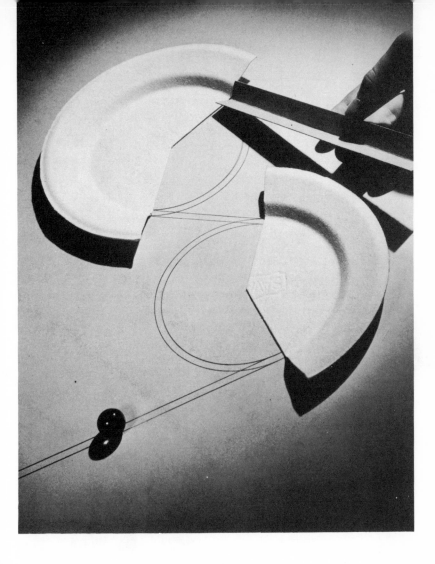

of the plate as shown above. Set your marble whirling in a curve by letting it roll down the incline at the top onto the circular wall of the bottom of the plate. (If the marble goes too fast, it will climb right over the side of the plate, just as a speeding car climbs over a bank that is not steep enough.) When the marble reaches the other edge, does it continue in a circle or fly outward from the center? Neither! It goes over in a perfectly straight line to the second portion of the plate, where it is forced into a circular motion again—only finally to shoot off once more in a straight line!

73

Why Ropes Break under Light Loads

Why do clotheslines and hammock ropes so often break under light loads? One reason can easily be demonstrated. Tie two rubber bands together and fasten a pocketknife, or other light weight, to the juncture. If you then hold the bands nearly parallel (see upper left-hand photograph opposite), the weight hardly stretches them. Spread the bands, as at upper right, and they stretch slightly more. Try, however, to straighten out the bands. You get the surprising result shown in the photograph at the bottom of the page. You can't straighten them further. The forces needed to support the small weight rapidly become so great that the bands will break!

By drawing a series of parallelograms, such as those below, you can illustrate how the forces necessary to sustain the knife increase drastically as the angle between them flattens. Let the vertical line represent the force that must be held up, and the lines showing the angle of the bands the forces that must be applied. To determine the forces on the bands just divide the length of the latter by the length of the former, and multiply the result by the weight of the knife.

At the left, the vertical line is the same length as the band lines. If the knife weighs 4 ounces, then each band pulls with a 4-ounce force. At the right, the band lines are each five times as long as the knife line. Hence, each band strains with a force of 20 ounces. From this point on, the forces climb steeply. Even the strongest ropes or cables would snap before you could apply sufficient force to make them absolutely horizontal.

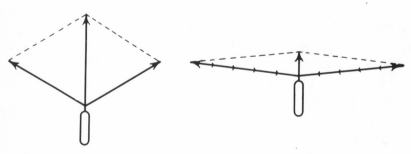

74

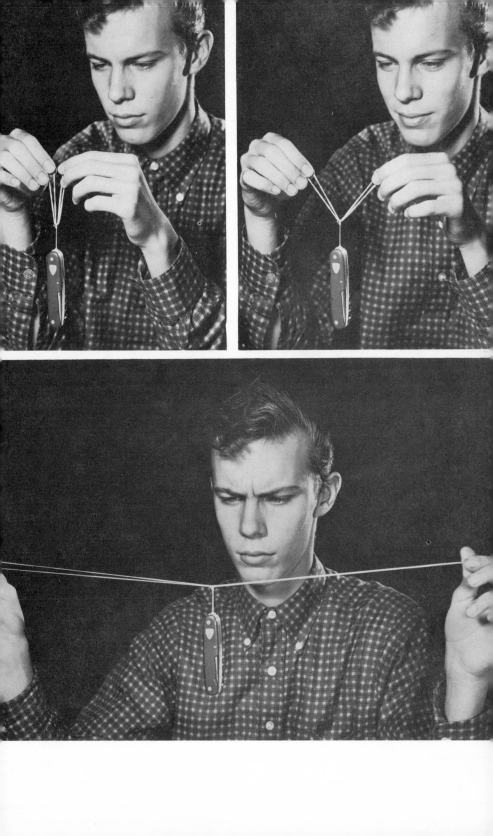

SOUND WAVES AND RESONANCE

How Sound Waves Travel

How do sound waves get from their source to your ear? Certainly not on gentle breezes, nor by any other method that involves the transfer of physical substance from the origin to you. For you can hear sounds even when the wind is blowing against them, and no physical substance is subtle enough to carry a peddler's yawp through closed windows and 10-inch walls!

You can get an idea of how sound waves do travel by performing this surprising little stunt. Clamp a coin to the table (or simply hold it down firmly), as shown at right, above, and place another coin to its left, just touching it. If you now snap a third coin so that it strikes sharply the opposite edge of the clamped one, the second coin jumps smartly away.

Although the clamped coin does not shift a fraction of an inch, energy from the motion of the third coin is passed right through it. This is done by means of a compressional wave. The edge of the fixed coin is first squeezed by the impact of the coin snapped against it. The squeeze impulse is then passed to the neighboring particles; they pass it on in their turn; and so down the line, until the particles at the opposite edge of the coin finally pass the impulse to the coin that's free to move.

It is by means of a similar game of pass-it between particles of air or of any other physical substance that sound gets from one place to another—even through ear stopples and locked doors! The source of sound is always some vibrating body—a violin string, a drumhead, an organ pipe, a tomcat's vocal cords—which imparts its vibrations to the air particles immediately surrounding it. These pass on the impulse, through particle after particle of air, until the original energy is completely spent. Although sound may travel for miles, the particles that convey it move only a tiny amount and end up exactly where they started.

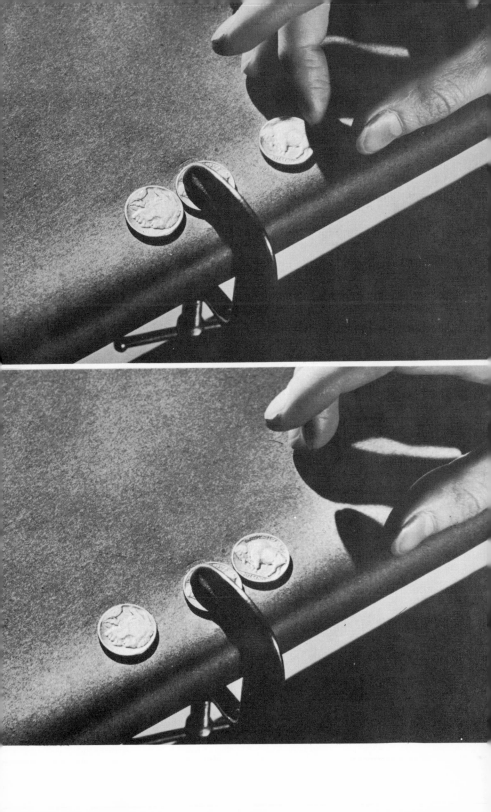

Sound Cannot Travel through a Vacuum

No matter how powerful, sound waves can never be used to speak to the Man in the Moon or to communicate with the inhabitants of Mars. For, unlike light and radio waves, sound waves must have a gas, liquid, or solid to carry them and hence can't travel beyond the earth's atmosphere. The "music of the spheres" is really a vast symphony of electromagnetic waves rather than waves of sound.

In 1660, Robert Boyle first proved that sound couldn't penetrate a vacuum. You can perform a simplified version of Boyle's experiment with a small Pyrex flask (a vacuum coffeepot bottom, as used on page 5, will do), a pencil, and a tiny bell. Tie the bell loosely to one end of the pencil by means of a rubber band. Push the other end of the pencil into a stopper which fits the flask snugly. Now pour a little water into the flask and boil until all the air is driven out. Remove the flask and stopper it the instant the steam stops expanding. When the water has cooled, shake the flask near your ear. The sound of the bell is almost inaudible, because the condensed steam has produced a partial vacuum. Let air into the flask again, and the tinkle can be heard clearly.

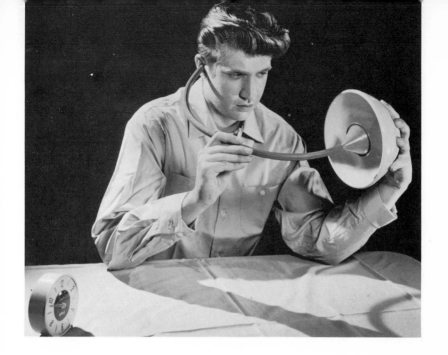

How Radio "Dishes" Spot Distant Stars

Giant dish-shaped radio telescopes are the newest and most sensitive "ears" of the Age of Space. Already they have followed signals from the tiny radio of Pioneer V more than 22,000,000 miles, caught radio waves from colliding galaxies over 6,000,000,000 *light years* away. They make feeble radio waves stronger by collecting them over a large area and then bringing them to a focus, just as the lens of an optical telescope collects and focuses light waves.

Although you would need expensive and complex equipment to demonstrate the principle of the radio telescope with actual radio waves, you can easily do so with sound waves. For a collector and reflector use a mixing bowl. To convey the collected waves to your ear use a small funnel with its stem inserted in one end of a two-foot length of rubber tubing.

To operate your sound-wave "telescope," aim the face of the bowl toward a source of weak but high-pitched sound, such as a ticking clock. Put the open end of the tube to one ear and move the mouth of the funnel into and out of the bowl. At one particular point—the focus—the ticking will be loud and clear.

79

Sound Waves Cancel Each Other

Strike the tines of a dinner fork sharply on the edge of the table and then hold them close to your ear. If you hold the fork vertically and twist it slowly, you notice a strange effect. Through one portion of the rotation, the high-pitched note of the vibrating fork dims out until it becomes almost inaudible. Continue the rotation, however, and it again increases in strength. As you keep on twisting the fork, the sound dims and grows loud again and again.

What is the reason? The sound waves that leave the opposite sides of the fork are caused to go into step and then out again, in relation to your ear, as the fork is turned. When the peaks of the waves overlap, the sound is increased; when a peak is superimposed on a trough, the waves cancel each other.

Hear through Your Teeth

You can not only hear sounds through the medium of your external ear but also through the bones of your head. This principle is applied in hearing devices for persons whose hearing nerves and inner ear are in working condition but who are deaf because of injury or disease of the external hearing apparatus. You can prove it by striking the tines of a dinner fork on the table and then quickly and firmly touching the handle to the bone just behind your ear. A distinct sound is heard. Repeat, touching other bones in your head. The relative loudness of the sound will depend largely upon the amount of insulating flesh covering the bone. For the most powerful result (as any dentist's patient might guess) clamp the fork handle firmly between your teeth!

Resonance Works Wonders

Whenever you tune your radio, push someone in a swing, or hear a picture rattle as certain notes are struck on the piano you come face to face with *resonance*, the big vibration that results when a small force is applied repeatedly, at exactly the right time, to any system that will vibrate.

In your radio set the force consists of weak electrical impulses caught from the air. When the set is not in resonance, or "tune," these impulses affect it feebly. When tuned to a state of reso-

nance, however, the impulses swing back and forth so freely that they may readily be transformed into audible speech and music. A small physical force, repeated at the swing's natural period, sends the swing higher and higher. If the picture rattles, it is because sound waves impinge upon it at its own rate of vibration.

You can demonstrate the principle of resonance convincingly by suspending a heavy book by two long cords and blowing on it with your breath. If your puffs are timed carefully to coincide with its natural period of vibration, the book can soon be made to swing strongly.

"Sound of the Sea" Is Due to Resonance

Did you ever put a sea shell to your ear to hear the "sound of the sea"? Did it strike you as odd that the sea should roar with a deep bass voice from big shells while it shrilled high soprano from little ones? The reason for both the sound and its pitch is resonance. The air within any enclosed space of moderate size vibrates more easily at one definite pitch than another; the bigger the space, the lower the pitch, and vice versa. Now the air around you, especially in cities, is full of a mixture of sounds of different pitch. When you put a shell to your ear, what you hear is merely an amplification of any sound from the hubbub that corresponds to the shell's own natural pitch! You can treat yourself to a whole chorus of "sea-roar" sounds by listening to tumblers, jars, cans, and boxes of different sizes.

Sympathetic Milk Bottles

Resonance accounts also for the jigging of knickknacks on the corner shelf when the radio coloratura hits high C and the rattling of pots and pans in sympathy with a lusty sneeze. Sound vibrations, which are in accord with the natural rate of vibration of the shelf, knickknacks, pots, or pans, set these things into resonant movement. With the help of two milk bottles, you can demonstrate just how such sympathetic response works. Have a friend hold the mouth of one bottle close to his ear without obstructing the opening. Now blow strongly across the mouth of the other bottle until you produce a strong, clear note. Every time you do this, resonant vibrations are set up in the second bottle. These produce a weaker, though similar, note which your friend can hear distinctly.

Pipe Organs and Aeolian Harps

When you fill a jar with water, your ears as well as your eyes tell you when it's nearly full. For the song of the falling water climbs right up the scale as the water rises until, finally, the pitch gets so high that you know the jar is ready to overflow.

Here we have one more example of resonance. As it falls into the jar, the water produces a mixture of sounds. The air column above the water level, like the space in the sea shell, selects and amplifies the sound that corresponds to its own natural pitch. As the water rises and the column of air shortens, the pitch goes higher and higher.

By filling a series of small soda bottles with different amounts of water, as shown above, you can utilize this principle to make a "pipe organ," on which, with a little dexterity, you can play real tunes to entertain your friends. This time you set the air columns vibrating by blowing across the tops of the bottles. Fill the first bottle about one-third full and add water, little by little, until your blowing makes it sound out with a low "do." Tune other bottles similarly, making the scale as long as you want.

Genuine organ pipes work on exactly the same principle as the "pipes" of this bottle organ. Air forced into the lower end of an organ pipe impinges on a sharp edge at the front of the pipe. Mixed air vibrations are set up about this edge. The vibrations then act in turn on the air column in the pipe, which amplifies the vibration corresponding to its own pitch.

In both your bottle organ and a real organ, the original vibrations set up—across the necks of the bottles and the edges of the pipes respectively—are due to irregular air currents, or eddies. (Remember those things the airplane and speed-car designers are so anxious to eliminate?) Air speeding across the necks and edges can't flow smoothly; hence it produces a fluctuating pressure which causes them to vibrate. Telephone wires and aeolian harps "sing" for the same reason. You can hear such vibrations with the device shown below. Flatten the end of a short metal tube until the opening is $\frac{1}{16}$ inch across. Fasten to the tube a loop of bell wire, so that a flattened portion is held about $\frac{1}{2}$ inch in front of the tube. To hear the wind sing, connect this tube to your ear with a rubber tube and hold the nozzle in front of an electric fan.

IT'S DONE WITH LIGHT AND MIRRORS

How Bright Is That Light?

When we speak of the candle power of an electric-light bulb, we mean exactly that. In the early days of electricity, the light produced by the newfangled bulbs was measured against that of a candle made to standard specifications. Later, oil and gas flames were substituted for real candles. Today, special carbon-filament bulbs, operated under rigidly controlled conditions, serve as international standards of light.

Since the beginning of the century, the efficiency of lighting units has increased amazingly. The carbon-filament bulbs of the early 1900's consumed about 4 watts of energy for every candle power of light they gave out. Today, modern tungsten lamps give the same amount of light for less than a single watt, while fluorescent tubes often give more than 3 candle power per watt.

The comparative intensity of light sources is measured by an instrument called a *photometer*. One of the simplest of these, designed by the Irish physicist Joly, can easily be made from two blocks of paraffin wax, a square of tin foil, and a ruler or yardstick. Cut the blocks from ordinary paraffin of the type used for home canning; make them of equal size and approximately square. Warm one of the faces of each block and press between these warmed faces a smooth piece of tin foil. When the wax has cooled, the two blocks and the tin foil form a solid unit.

If you now darken the room and put this composite block between any two lights, you can easily compare the intensity of the lights by its aid. Put the lesser light (one candle, for instance) at a distance of about 6 inches from one face of the block, as shown in the photograph, and note the brightness shown at the block's edge. Then move the other light away from or toward the other face of the block until the illumination at the edge seems equal on both sides.

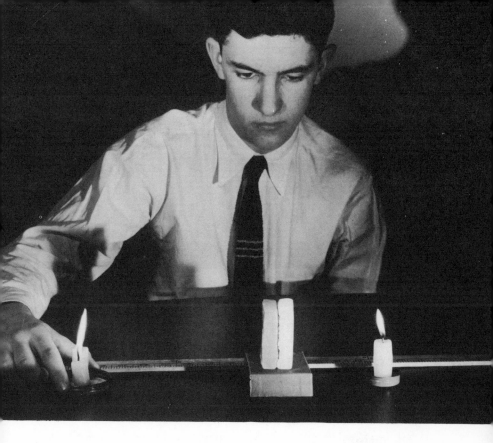

All you have to do now to find out the comparative brightness of the two lights is to measure the distance from each light to the face of the block nearest it. As light increases or decreases not according to its simple distance from the source but according to the *square* of this distance, you then square these figures and divide the larger product by the smaller.

Suppose, for example, you use a single candle for the lesser light and place it 6 inches from one face of the block. The greater light to be tested is a 25-watt tungsten bulb, and you have to place it 29 inches from the other face of the block to balance the brightness. Multiply 29 by 29 and you get 841; divide this by 36, the square of 6, and the result is 23+, the candle power of the bulb. Only fairly concentrated sources of light, such as candles, lamps, tungsten bulbs, and arcs can be tested by this method. The light from fluorescent tubes is distributed over too large an area to give accurate results.

See a Spectrum with a Record

Rainbow-colored *spectra*—created by splitting up light by bouncing it off finely-ruled gratings—have long been used to identify substances on earth. Today they are also used to study stars and planets and to measure distances and motions through space.

Gratings in the best spectroscopes contain from 15,000 to 30,000 lines per inch, ruled with a diamond on glass or metal. Light to be analyzed enters the instrument through a narrow slit parallel to the grating. The lines *diffract*, or scatter light of different colors different amounts and so produce a spectrum.

Original gratings cost a fortune, but you can see how they work with only a long-playing record and a 25-watt straight-filament bulb (which will serve as both a light source and a slit). Mount the bulb upright and, from a distance of several feet, sight along the record with one eye, as shown above. Observe either the grooves near your eye or those nearer the light. At the proper position, you will see a reflection of the lamp filament, flanked on each side by a spectrum. Because the grooves are fewer, the colors will not be spread as much as with a real grating, but they will be vivid.

Sodium Light Blacks Out Colors

By means of a sodium light, which you can conjure up in two shakes, you can demonstrate dramatically what happens to vari-colored objects when viewed by light of a single color.

Put a few lumps of borax (sodium borate) into a jar cover and moisten them with denatured alcohol. Now, in a room otherwise completely dark, light the alcohol and observe a colored picture by means of its light. At first the colors seem almost normal. As soon as the borax heats up, however, all colors but yellow mysteriously vanish, the rest changing to tones of yellowish gray! Sodium light contains no color except a very narrow band of yellow. Hence, no other colors can be seen by it.

Sodium-vapor lamps are being tested on highways, partly be-cause they give more light for less money and partly in the belief that their elimination of color improves contrast and makes night vision easier.

The left-hand tumbler contains water; the right-hand, a cleaning fluid. Submerge similar glass mugs in these liquids, and what happens?

Now You See It!

In fairy tales and legends you have probably read of the cloak that would make its wearer invisible. Although science can't yet equal this feat of the legend writers—at least as far as human beings and other opaque objects are concerned—it can readily produce a "cloak" that will make *glass* disappear.

How this cloak works is shown in the photographs above and on the next page. Its material is the water-clear liquid that fills the right-hand tumbler in each picture. The liquid in the other tumbler, introduced for contrast, is just plain water. To demonstrate, two similar solid objects of clear glass are submerged in the liquids in the two tumblers. The result? The object in water remains almost as visible as it was in air; the object in the other fluid vanishes!

Why? Glassware, no matter how clear, can generally be seen

The mug in the water remains visible, while the other one vanishes!
Matching indexes of refraction of glass and fluid explain the mystery.

because of light reflected from its surfaces and refracted within it. Find some way to eliminate reflection and refraction, and the glass will disappear.

In the present feat of optical sleight of hand, that is exactly what has been done. Our scientific "cloak of invisibility" turns out to be a liquid that bends light to the same extent (has the same *index of refraction,* to put it more scientifically) as does the glass immersed in it. Put glass into such a liquid and, lo! the glass vanishes as if it were imbedded in a block of its own substance.

In the photographs, tetrachloroethylene, a dry-cleaning fluid obtainable at chemical supply houses, was used. Benzol would also serve. Since the index of refraction varies with different kinds of glass, some glass may remain slightly visible in the liquid, as does the little mug shown above. Under different lighting, however, it can't be seen.

Blue Sky and Orange Sunsets

The fact that the sky is blue and the sun orange at sunrise and sunset is due to the selective scattering of light. As white light from the sun streams through the atmosphere, the shorter violet and blue rays, being more easily deflected, are bent from their course by particles of dust and moisture and by irregularities in the density of the air itself. This scattering of light causes the sky to appear blue and the sun slightly yellow.

With a flashlight and water containing a few drops of milk, you can witness how the scattering takes place. Darken the room and look directly through the glass at the flashlight beam. The light appears yellow, due to the scattering of short blue rays by the suspended particles of milk. If, without moving the light, you look through the side of the glass, the liquid appears blue.

At dawn and dusk the sun deepens to orange or red because longer wave lengths of light are scattered as the rays pass through more miles of atmosphere. By adding more milk to the water, the rays from your flashlight will deepen in the same way.

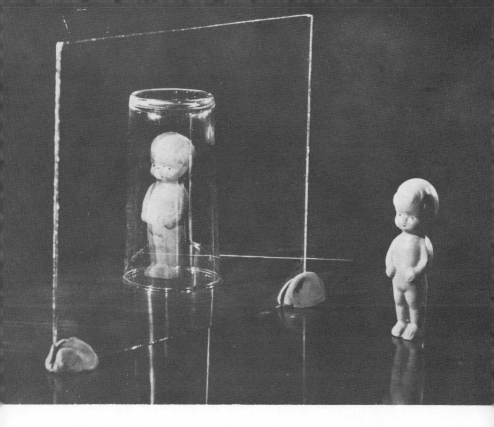

Where Is the Image in the Looking Glass?

Although you can't find the reflected image of an object by looking behind a mirror, the position of this image is apparently fixed in space. To prove this, stand a little doll or other object in front of a plain sheet of glass which substitutes for an ordinary mirror. Then, watching the reflected image, maneuver an inverted tumbler behind the glass until the image appears to be inside the tumbler, as shown above. By this strategy you can trap the image and measure its exact position with a ruler.

No matter where the doll has been placed, you will discover that the image is just as far behind the mirror as the doll is in front, in a line perpendicular to the plane of the glass. Regardless of your point of observation, the position of the image stays put.

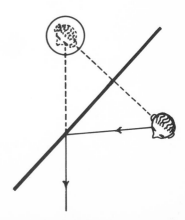

95

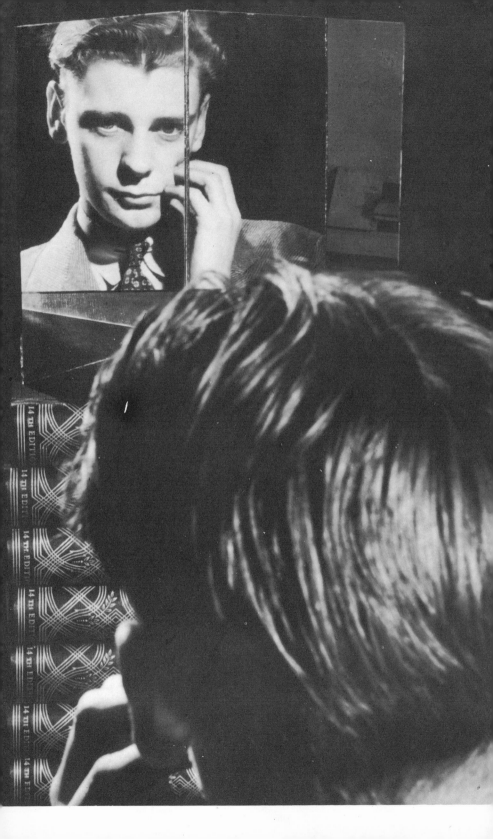

See Yourself as Others See You

Do you know how you look to your friends? Don't say "yes," just because you've gazed into a mirror. Ordinary mirrors turn you completely around. But if you take two ordinary mirrors and set them up exactly at right angles to each other, as shown in the diagram below and the photograph on the opposite page, you can get a true picture of yourself as others see you.

To prove that this mirror combination sets things right side to, hold a book page in front of it; instead of appearing backward, as they would in a single mirror, the letters and words are lined up in their proper order. You, however, look strange. Turn your head one way, and your new reflected double perversely turns the other. Try to shave or to make up, and you find your face cut up or covered with greasy smears before the session is over—for your hand always appears on the wrong side of the image and moves the wrong way!

Oddly enough, no part of the self that you see in the pair of mirrors comes originally from the single mirror in which it is seen. Remove either mirror, and you have no image at all! What really happens is this. The image on the left side of your face is caught by the left-hand mirror and is reflected over to the right-hand mirror, which in turn reflects it back to your eye. The same holds true for the image on the right side.

If you want to experiment further with mirror images, move closer to the mirrors. If you move close enough, two additional images appear, one of the left and one of the right side of your face. That a total of three images should appear can be predicted mathematically. Here is the rule: To find the number of images produced by two mirrors set at an angle to each other, divide 360 (the number of degrees in a circle) by the angle; then subtract 1. It's easy. Divide 360 by 90 and you get 4; subtract 1 and you have 3. By reducing the angle to 60 degrees, you will get five images; to 45 degrees, seven images; and so on.

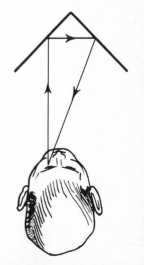

Shaving Mirror Produces Phantom Flowers

It's hard to believe, but the flowers shown in the vase on the opposite page are not in the vase at all! They are mere phantoms, projected by a concave shaving mirror into the space above the vase, much as moving pictures are thrown on a screen. Like a lens, a mirror of this type can project a real image.

You can duplicate this almost incredible illusion by setting up the simple objects shown above. Fasten a few flowers upside down to the underside of a book, support the book on several other books, then place a small vase directly above the flowers. The concave mirror should be so aimed that its center is in line with the top of the vase. (Unfortunately, the curvature of some shaving mirrors is so poorly formed that they will not produce a good image. Whether your mirror will or not can be determined only by experiment.) Darken the room, except for one strong light from a desk lamp or small spotlight, which should play on the flowers.

Now sight along the top of the vase toward the mirror, keeping your eye at least a foot behind the vase. By carefully adjusting the distance and angle of the mirror, you will find a position where the

flowers appear life size, upright, and as if they were actually coming out of the vase. If you doubt the realness of the image, you can
take a photograph of it, as has been done for this book!

99

When observed from this angle, the undersurface of clear water appears as bright and opaque as polished silver. A trick of refraction keeps you from seeing out through it.

Clear Water Is Sometimes Opaque

Would you believe that under certain conditions you can't see through the smooth surface of clear water? If you doubt this statement, just hold a glass of water a little above your eyes and to the side, as shown on the opposite page, and try to see up through the surface. It's impossible. The undersurface of the water has become as opaque and as bright as a shining, silvered mirror!

A trick of light, called *total internal reflection*, keeps you from seeing out. When light rays, traveling at an angle off the vertical, try to get from water to air they are bent at the surface. The greater the angle, the more they are bent. When the angle becomes about 48 degrees (for water) the rays cannot get through the surface at all but are bent back into the water. Because of this phenomenon, a fish or a diver can see out of water only through a circle that extends about 48 degrees to each side of the vertical.

A puzzling parlor trick involving total reflection is shown below. Place a coin in the bottom of a deep dish filled with water and cover with a small glass. If you let the glass fill with water as you lower it, the coin remains visible. Lower the glass straight down, however, so that the air in it keeps out water, and the coin disappears, due to internal reflection at the water-air surface. (The spectator must never look straight down through the glass, of course, as from there the coin is always visible.)

Flying Saucers—or Mirage?

You don't have to fly a plane or stand watch over a desert to catch a glimpse of flying saucers. You can see them at home, using just a milk bottle filled with water, a flashlight, and a few other common gadgets. As an example, the photograph at the top of the facing page is of a homemade version of the famous "Lubbock Lights," originally snapped over Lubbock, Texas, in 1951.

Flying saucers that cannot be accounted for as pure hoaxes or as misinterpretations of known flying objects are not *necessarily* spaceships or missiles from another world. Dr. Donald H. Menzel, noted astrophysicist, suggests that they may be optical ghosts—types of mirage—projected into the sky by tricks of light.

In some cases, the sky phenomena may originate as automobile headlights, searchlights, or distant street lights. Striking a layer of warm air above, the rays from these sources are reflected downward toward the earth. To an observer on the ground, this bending of the light rays makes the light source seem to be overhead. In other cases, a pilot flying over a layer of warm air sees the light from the sun, a planet, or a brightly lighted cloud bent upward. Such a light seems to be below him. Under either condition, the ghost light would seem to move if its source—or the observer or the layer of warm air—moves.

Flying saucers are probably seen most frequently over desert areas because the atmospheric conditions necessary to produce these strange mirages are most common there. During the day, the air and the ground get very hot. At night, and also under certain cloud conditions during the day, the ground cools rapidly by radiating its heat toward the sky. As a result, the air for a few feet up cools off by contact with the cool earth, but the air higher up stays warm. Because light rays travel faster in light warm air than they do in cold dense air, they are bent back into the cold air whenever they strike the layer of warm air at an angle.

Although you can't experiment with miles of atmosphere in your home, you can show the principle by substituting water for the cold dense air and ordinary air for the warm light air. Support

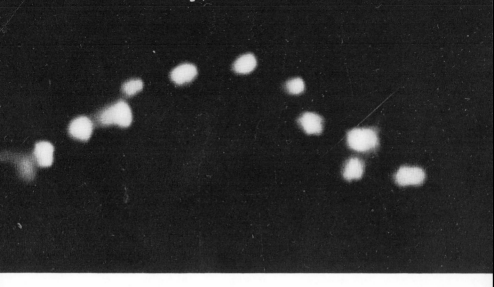

a square milk bottle, partly full of water, so you can see the under side of the water surface. Mask a flashlight with a piece of cardboard having a ¼-inch hole in it and aim the light at this surface, as shown at the left, below. Amazingly, the light seems to be coming from *above* the surface of the water. In the same way, though less abruptly, a warm air surface above cold air could bend back a distant ground light so that from the ground it would look like a distant saucer in the sky.

The Lubbock Lights were possibly ghosts of distant street lights turned down by such a surface. Undulations in the surface made them move. The simulation of such lights shown above was made by masking the flashlight with a cardboard square pricked with pinholes and viewing the reflections as just described.

To see how pilots flying in cold air above a layer of warm air can witness a similar mirage, but in reverse, pour out some of the water and float several inches of mineral oil on what is left. Then shine your masked light on the oil-water surface, as shown below, right. The light will seem to be coming from *below* the surface.

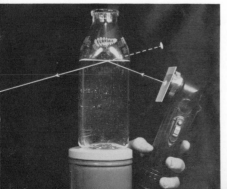 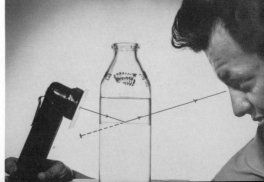

ELECTRICITY AND MAGNETISM

Electric Light—Free for the Rubbing!

Do you think you lack energy? If it's electric energy you are worrying about, don't believe it for a minute. With the help of an ordinary fluorescent lighting tube and just enough vigor to waggle the tube a few times on your coat sleeve, you can prove to yourself that you are really a human dynamo!

Because electric charges leak off rapidly in moist air, this feat works best on a cold night, when the indoor temperature is high and the humidity low. Darken the room and grasp one end of the fluorescent tube with one hand and rub the tube lightly but rapidly on the other arm. Inside a few seconds—despite the fact that the tube is not connected with any source of electricity except yourself—the tube lights up brightly!

Although you may prefer to pay your electric company a tenth of a cent an hour to light the tube effortlessly from the house mains, the method just described is not only startling but demonstrates vividly that electricity can be conjured up from more sources than batteries, generators, and the plug in the wall.

Nothing new, electricity by rubbing was the first form ever produced by man. As long ago as 600 B.C., Thales of Miletus knew that rubbed amber would attract light substances. From the Greek word for amber, *elektron*, we get our term "electricity."

Today we know that *all* substances are full of electricity. Ordinarily we are unconscious of it because the positive and negative charges that make it up are exactly balanced. By rubbing certain substances together, though, you may detach electrons from one surface and transfer them to the other, upsetting the balance. Then things begin to happen. After scuffing over a thick-piled carpet you get a jolt when you shake hands with a friend; sparks crackle in your hair as you try to comb it; rubbed paper sticks to the wall; and fluorescent tubes light up mysteriously!

104

On a dry winter's night you can light a fluorescent tube merely by rubbing it on your sleeve. Rubbing removes electrons from the glass, unbalances its electrical charge, and so produces surges of current.

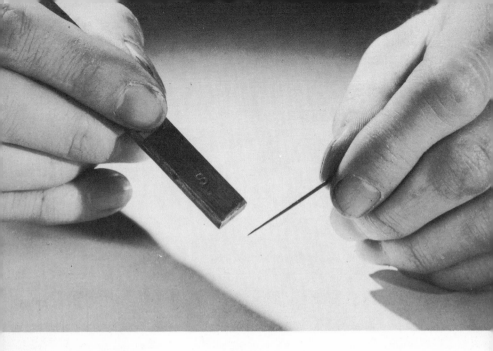

A Compass in a Minute

Simply by rubbing a steel sewing needle on a magnet and then floating the needle on a cork in a cup of water, you can make a compass as good as those by which men steered ships for centuries. It took the ancients more than 1,700 years to discover the north-south pointing property of a magnet and put it to regular use. You can duplicate their earliest compass in a minute.

Use just one pole of either a bar or horseshoe magnet. If you want the point of the needle to point north, stroke the needle across the south pole of the magnet, starting from the eye and ending at the point. Stroke always in the same direction and move the needle away from the magnet to bring it into position for the next stroke. The end of the needle that last leaves the magnet pole will have a polarity opposite to that of the pole.

To make your compass, merely balance the magnetized needle on a flat cork and float the cork on water in a cup. If you have done a good job, the point of the needle will swing around until it aims toward the north magnetic pole of the earth.

The history of magnets and magnetism goes back so far that in the earliest accounts it is hard to separate fact from fiction. A

106

strange stone that could attract iron was known before the time of Thales. Legend tells of a Cretan shepherd who was so strongly drawn to earth by the nails in his shoes and the iron on the tip of his staff that he could hardly drag himself away. Upon digging a hole beneath his feet, he discovered magnetic ore. Greek tellers of tall tales speak further of magnetic mountains so powerful that they could pull the nails from ships over great distances!

According to the Roman poet Lucretius, writing in 60 B.C., the name *magnes* (from which our "magnet" is derived) came from Magnesia, a district in Asia Minor where magnetic ore was plentiful. No one knows where or when the directional ability of a suspended or floated magnet was first recognized. The pivoted-type compass came into use in the thirteenth century. Before that time, compasses were described as magnets mounted on wood and floated on water; as floating "iron fish" which "pointed north with their heads and south with their tails"; and as magnetized needles floated on splinters or cork, such as the one you can readily make.

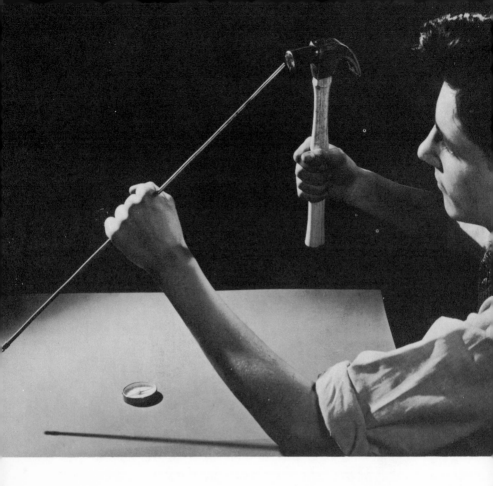

Magnetism from the Earth's Field

Because the earth acts as a great magnet, pieces of iron or steel lying along the magnetic meridian often become magnetized by induction. If the objects are jolted while in this position their molecules get lined up particularly easily. You can get some free magnetism, therefore, merely by hammering one end of an iron rod (a solid iron curtain rod will do) while holding it in a north-south position. Tilt its north end downward if you are in the Northern Hemisphere and its south end downward if you are in the Southern. After a few smart blows, you can prove that the rod has magnetic poles by bringing the ends near a compass. To reverse these poles, turn the rod end for end and tap again. To demagnetize the rod, just tap it when held in an east-west direction.

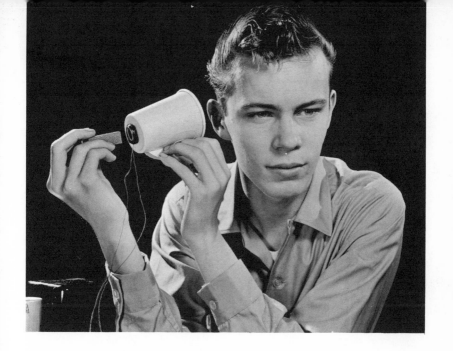

A Loudspeaker from a Cup

The voice from the loudspeaker of your hi-fi record player, radio, and TV set depends on magnetism. A coil of wire, attached to a cone of specially treated paper, is suspended in the field of a powerful permanent magnet. Electrical impulses from the amplifier, varying in frequency and intensity with vibrations cut on a record or sent by radio, flow through the coil. These produce a changing magnetism in it and so cause it to be attracted and repelled by the fixed magnet. The cone, vibrating with the coil, moves the air around it to create the speech and music that you hear.

You can make a working model of a speaker with nothing but a small Alnico bar magnet, a dozen feet of number 26 (or thereabouts) magnet wire, and a paper cup. Wind the wire into a 1-inch coil of about 50 turns, leaving several feet at each end for connections. Bind the turns with tape and cement one edge of the coil to the bottom of the cup. If you now connect the coil to your hi-fi amplifier, or across the speaker terminals of your radio or TV, and bring one end of the bar magnet near or into it, the cup will mysteriously talk and sing, reproducing in sound the character of the electrical waves fed into it.

How to Make Crystals That Talk

Twist or squeeze certain crystals, and they generate electricity; charge these crystals electrically, and they contract or expand depending upon the direction of the charge. This curious *piezoelectric* effect (from the Greek *piezein*, "to press") was first noted in 1880 by the famous co-discoverer of radium, Pierre Curie, and his brother Jacques. Today, piezoelectric crystals operate microphones and hi-fi pickups, earphones and loudspeakers. Vibrated by powerful high-frequency currents, they are helping to create a thousand wonders in the fast-growing science of ultrasonics.

One of the commonest piezoelectric crystals is potassium sodium tartrate, Rochelle salt. With four ounces of this chemical from your local drug store, you can grow a large, beautifully shaped crystal that will produce voice and music when connected to your radio or record player.

To grow your crystal, first dissolve the Rochelle salt in a glass containing 3½ ounces of warm water. Pour 1 ounce of the solution into a shallow dish, cover the dish with a thin cloth to keep out dust, and set it in a quiet spot where the temperature is from about 70 to 75 degrees Fahrenheit and stays constant.

Next day, look to see if crystals have formed. If you find many tiny crystals covering the bottom of the dish, dissolve these again by placing the dish in a pan of warm water and stirring the solution. If a few well shaped larger crystals have formed, let these continue to grow until they are about ¼ inch long. Leave the best one in the dish as the "seed" for your final crystal, remove the others, and pour the remainder of the solution into the dish. Within a few

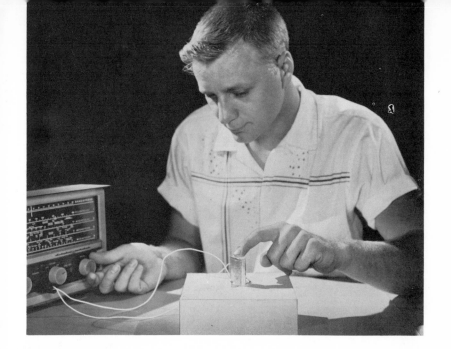

days to several weeks (depending upon variations in temperature, humidity, and ventilation) you should have a crystal about 2 inches long, as shown at left, below.

Remove this crystal from the solution, dry it with a cloth, and bind an electrode (in the form of a piece of aluminum foil, cut as shown at the left of the photo at right, below) to each of its two wider faces by means of cellophane tape. Fold over the two flaps on the extensions to the electrodes to make connecting lugs, and fold the ends of these over the bare ends of two wires connected to the earphone jack of a radio or the output of a record player. To make the crystal "talk," just press it down with a finger on the top of an upside-down cardboard box (to act as a sounding board) and turn up your radio or player to high volume.

Volta, Volts, and a Penny Battery

With only a penny, a galvanized iron washer, and a bit of blotting paper soaked in salt water or vinegar to help you, you can in a few seconds conjure up a working model of an apparatus which once amazed the world and changed the whole course of electrical history. The modern dry battery in your flashlight or portable radio is its great-great-grandchild. Without it, physicists might still be puttering around over such impracticable sources of electricity as lightning bolts, charged amber, and electric eels.

To make this battery cell, merely squeeze the moistened blotting paper between the cent and the washer. You can't run a washing machine on its current or even light a small bulb, but you can definitely detect the current by means of the improvised meter as shown. Wind about fifty turns of fine insulated wire around a dime pocket compass. Adjust the compass so that its needle is normally parallel with the coil. Then connect one end of the coil to the washer and the other end to the cent. Immediately, the compass needle swings away from the normal. Reverse the connections, and the needle swings vigorously in the opposite direction!

Back in the 1780's, Aloisio Galvani, physician and professor of anatomy at Bologna, noticed that a frog's leg, lying on a metal plate, twitched violently when a wire of some different metal was touched to the crural nerve and to the plate. Galvani thought that in the nerve he had discovered a new source of electricity. It remained for his countryman, Alessandro Volta, to prove that some mysterious action between the dissimilar metals and the fluid in the leg was really responsible for the twitching. Volta found further that by piling up pairs of disks of different metals, separating the pairs with pieces of flannel moistened with dilute acetic acid, he could build up a surprisingly great electrical potential.

This "voltaic pile," which the inventor exhibited before Napoleon and the ablest physicists of Europe, was the first electric battery. It ushered in the era of "current," as distinguished from "static," electricity and foreshadowed developments which today

112

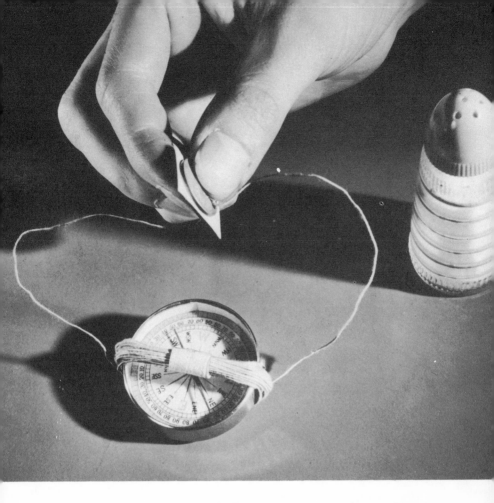

make electricity the mighty and ubiquitous servant of man. Every time you speak of "volt" or "voltage" you pay unconscious tribute to this great pioneer.

Volta never knew exactly how his batteries worked. Modern science has determined that their action is chemical. Separate two different metals by a conducting liquid that acts more strongly on one than on the other, and a movement of electrons takes place through the liquid. The metal least acted upon becomes charged to a higher electrical potential than the other. By connecting the two metals with a wire, an electric current flows through the wire from the metal of high potential to the one of low, much as water flows from a higher to a lower level. The difference of potential is expressed in terms of *voltage*.

A.C. and D.C. Write Their Signatures

Maybe the difference between direct current (d.c.) and alternating current (a.c.) is a mystery to you. By making each visibly identify itself you can get better acquainted.

Wet a strip of cloth in water containing cornstarch and a little potassium iodide (obtainable at a drug or photographic store). Squeeze out excess solution and smooth the cloth over the up-turned back of a metal pan or pie plate. The cloth will serve as your writing paper and the pan as your desk.

To force a current to write its name, merely touch one wire from the source to the pan and draw the bare tip of the other wire firmly over the cloth. (Use only three or four dry cells or the output of a bell-ringing or toy-train transformer for your current supply; current straight from the mains would be dangerous.) If the current is *direct*, as from a battery, its signature will be a single dark line, as shown in the photograph above; if *alternating*, as from

114

a transformer, the dark line will be broken by blank spaces, as shown above on this page.

How does this magic work? When an electric current is applied to a solution of potassium iodide, the compound is broken down so that potassium hydroxide appears at the negative terminal and free iodine at the positive. Iodine, in turn—wherever it is released —reacts with the starch to form a dark compound, which is responsible for the line.

Now direct current is merely electric current that flows continuously in a single direction. Apply such a current to cloth soaked in potassium iodide solution, and iodine is released constantly from the terminal as it is drawn along, if the terminal happens to be positive. (If no line appears, reverse the connections to the battery.) Alternating current, on the other hand, changes its direction of flow many times each second. Apply such current to the cloth, and iodine is released alternately from one side of the cloth and the other.

Electricity Traps Smoke and Dust

The Cottrell electric dust precipitator has long been saving American industry millions of dollars a year by recovering potassium salts, zinc, arsenic, selenium, and other chemical by-products which were on their way up factory chimneys as smoke. Today you can buy portable or built-in precipitators that will knock the dust out of the air in your office or home.

Here's how it works. Air containing dust or smoke particles is passed between wires and plates charged with electricity at high voltage. In passing, the particles attract ions, become charged themselves, and are attracted to the plates. From the plates they either fall into a receiver by gravity or are scraped off.

116

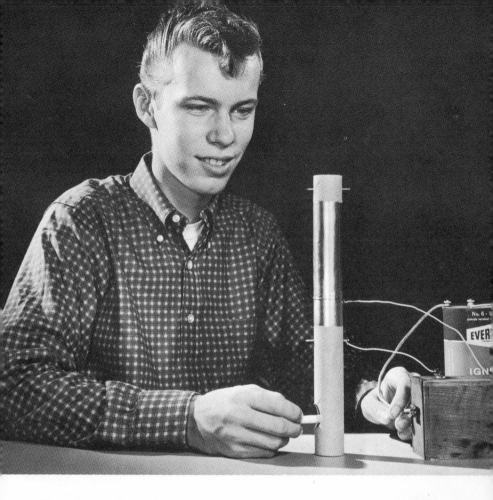

You can easily make a working model if you have a Model-T Ford spark coil (still obtainable from large auto supply houses) to provide the high voltage. The cardboard core of a roll of paper towels will serve as a chimney. Cut a 1-inch hole near one end, paste a 5-inch-wide strip of aluminum foil near the other, and support a thin wire down the center of the tube by means of two nails —the first thrust through the tube an inch above and the other an inch below the foil. Connect the foil to one high-voltage terminal of the spark coil and one of the nails to the other.

To demonstrate, thrust the lit end of a cigarette or stick of incense into the hole near the bottom of the tube while the current is off. Smoke pours from the top, as shown above left. Now start your spark coil working. Immediately smoke stops coming forth!

YOUR SENSES MAY FOOL YOU

Image in Eye Is Really Upside Down

Human creatures learn far more about the external world and their place in it by means of their vision than by means of all their other senses combined. The marvelous human eye, with its associated nerve and brain mechanism, takes in a multitude of mere vibrations of different frequencies and intensities and, by some imperfectly understood magic, translates these into a whole universe of light and shadow, color, movement, shape, and space. That such a complex instrument sometimes plays tricks on us and that even its ordinary workings often baffle the scientist does not detract in the least from its wonder.

One of the most amazing of the vision's tricks (a bit of sleight of hand which seems quite normal and not a trick at all until you begin to think seriously about it) enables us to see things upright and moving in the normal direction in which they actually move in space.

If you don't think upright vision is strange, compare your eye with a photographic camera which, from the optical standpoint, it resembles almost exactly. Each consists of a dark chamber having a lens in front and, at the back, a screen upon which images transmitted by the lens are focused. If you have ever looked at the image on the ground glass of a camera, however, you know that there the similarity stops abruptly. For whereas with your eye you see people and things standing on their feet and moving in the direction in which the actual people and things do move, on the ground glass they appear to stand on their heads and move backward instead of forward.

If camera and eye work on the same principle, why isn't the image on the retina upside down, too? Should you partially dissect an eyeball, you would find that it *is*! The images that fleet across the screen at the back of your eye are the same crazy, topsy-turvy

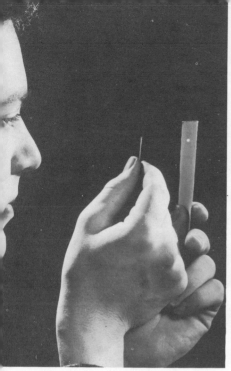 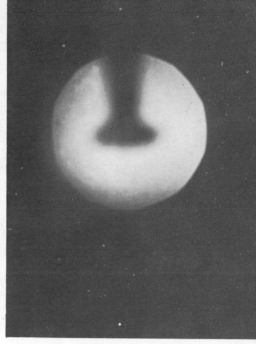

If you hold a pin so that it casts an erect shadow on your retina, *your mind will turn the shadow upside down, as shown above.*

images that you see in the camera. The fact that you don't see them that way is due to some mysterious turning-around process which takes place in your brain.

That retinal images are normally upside down and backward can be proved with the help of a pin and a card with a pinhole through it. Hold the card about 6 or 8 inches from one eye and sight through the hole toward some uniform light, such as a lamp or the sky. Then raise the pin vertically, as shown above, until the head comes between your eye and the light from the hole.

In this position, the eye lens cannot produce an inverted image of the pinhead; instead, the head merely blocks part of the widely diverging rays from the tiny hole and casts an *upright* shadow on the retina. But what do you see? A shadow that *descends* from the top of the lighted hole! Move the pin from *left to right,* and the shadow moves perversely from *right to left*! Instead of righting the normally inverted image in your eye, the brain in this case takes the right-side-up shadow and turns it upside down.

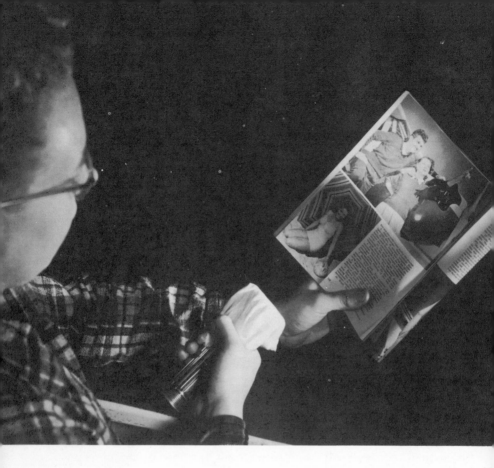

Green Light Can Be Seen the Longest

As light dims, the sensitivity of the human eye to color reverses itself. It is due to this "Purkinje effect" that the colors in a country-side seem to change as twilight falls. Reds black out first, while blues and violets appear relatively brighter than they do in day-light. Green is the last color to fade away. When the light becomes dim enough, color can't be distinguished at all.

You can prove this by covering the lens of a flashlight with thick-nesses of white cloth or tissue paper until you can barely see ob-jects by its light in a dark room. Under such dim illumination, the green and blue of a colored picture seem brighter than normal, while the red and yellow seem darker. By increasing the light gradually, you can find a point where the brilliance reverses itself.

120

Red Ink Is Sometimes Green

Thin films of some metals and solutions of aniline dyes seem mysteriously to change color merely depending on the way you look at them! In this case, the trickery is the fault of the substance, and not you. For instance, red ink made from certain dyes can appear green. Put a few drops on the bottom of a glass tumbler and look through it. It is definitely red. Now hold the ink so that light is reflected from its surface to your eye, as shown above. It is *green!* This strange effect is due to some sort of selective reflection of light at the surface, and the two colors exhibited are generally complementary.

You Can't Judge Distance with One Eye

The following stunt looks easy, but the results may surprise you. Close one eye and, holding two pencils not quite at arm's length, try to touch their tips together. To make the test purely one of vision, drop your arms out of position between each try. This simple manipulation becomes hard because we owe our ability to judge depth, or the distance of any object away from us, to the fact that ordinarily we use two eyes, which view the object from slightly different angles. When trained on it, they act like the two "eyes" of a range finder used to spot targets, or the smaller one on your camera. Objects appear three-dimensional because with two eyes we see partly around them. When one eye is eliminated, they seem to be flat and in the same plane.

Trick of Vision Explains Movies and TV

Just before your next program of slides or home movies, why not surprise your audience with a picture conjured up in mid-air on nothing but a whirling piece of string!

All you need is a 2-foot length of heavy white cord (venetian blind cord is excellent) with a small weight tied on one end to keep it taut. Holding the string by the free end, whirl it rapidly in a plane parallel with the projector lens. For best effect, focus the projector secretly on your whirling string and whirl the string later at the same spot; don't make the picture too large; and keep it well out out in the room so the image on the distant wall will be dim and out of focus.

How can you see a complete picture on a screen only a fraction of its width? By *persistence of vision*. Your eye continues to see an image for a moment after the stimulus has gone. As a result, a succession of partial images combine in your eye to form a whole picture. Because of this same quirk of sight, your eyes change a series of still pictures jerked in rapid succession before them into moving pictures and a varying beam of light traced swiftly in lines across a chemical screen into the familiar pictures of television.

123

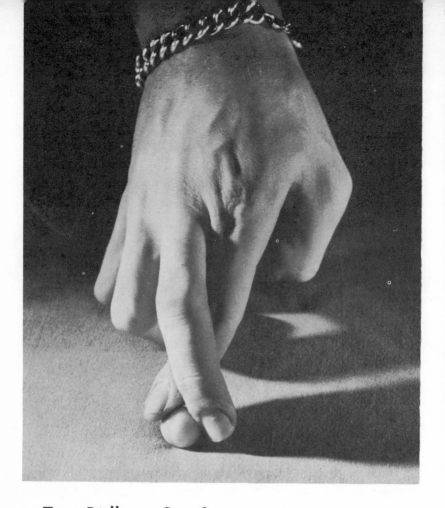

Two Balls or One?

Can you always believe what you feel with your fingers? If you think you can, try rolling a large marble or ping-pong ball between the tips of your first and second fingers, crossed as shown. Keep your eyes closed while you do so. Roll the ball so that it touches first one finger and then the other. Although your mind tells you that you have only one ball at your finger ends, your sense of touch tries desperately to convince you that there are two. Aristotle, the Greek scientist-philosopher, mentioned this illusion more than 300 years before the Christian Era. It is still a puzzler. When the fingers are crossed, sense stimuli come to the brain by unfamiliar paths, and the mind is thereby confused.

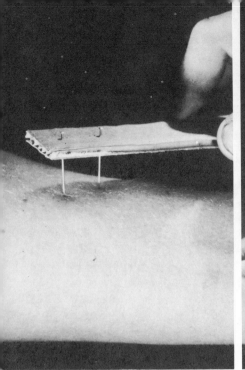
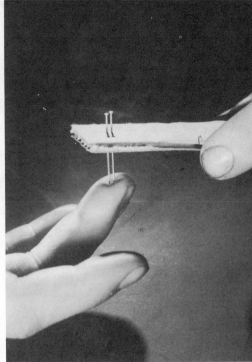

Sensitivity to Touch Varies

Our sensitivity to touch varies from one part of the body to another because our nerve endings are unequally distributed throughout the body's surface. On the tips of the fingers, where great sensitivity is necessary, the nerve endings are packed near together; on the lips and tip of the tongue they are still more closely concentrated. But on the back of the hand and arm and on other parts of the body where marked sensitivity is not needed, the endings are comparatively far apart.

To prove this, thrust two pins about 1 inch apart through a strip of heavy cardboard. Touch a blindfolded friend lightly on the back of the arm with the points, as shown at left. If he is normal, he will say that the point of only *one* pin touched him. You may be able to move the pins still farther apart before he realizes that there are two. But move the pins close together, as shown at right, and touch a finger tip, and your friend will note the two pins immediately. On the tip of the tongue, points closer than $\frac{1}{32}$ inch may readily be distinguished.

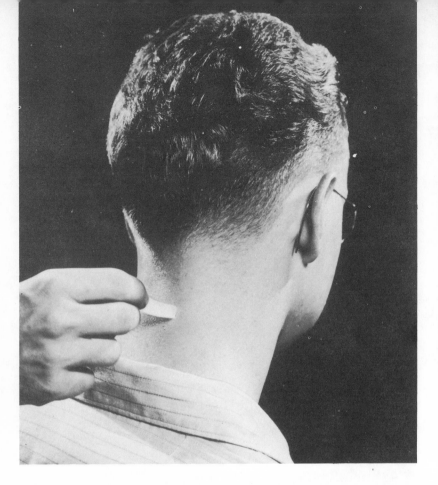

Is It Hot or Cold?

Sensation we think we feel is often governed by what we see. For instance, sensations of heat or cold which are intense enough to cause mild pain may be so similar that we say, "Ouch! that's hot!" or "Wow! that's cold!" merely because the appearance of the object that caused the sensation gives us the impression that it should be either hot or cold. Without the help of our eyes, we can easily be fooled. Here is a stunt to prove it. While in a group of smokers, secretly procure a piece of ice, one end of which has been chipped to about the diameter of a lead pencil. Dry the tip carefully and touch it quickly to the back of the neck of one of your friends. If you ask what all the excitement's about, he'll swear that you burned him with the lighted tip of a cigarette!

126

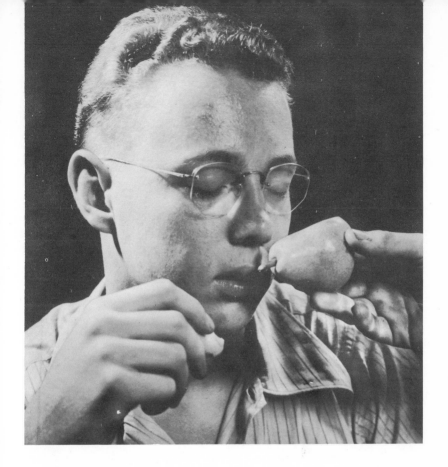

Taste Good? Maybe It's the Smell!

Grandmother knew what she was doing when she held Willie's nose to help him down his castor oil. Science now recognizes that the "taste" of many articles of food and medicine is really caused largely by its smell. True taste, a chemically initiated sensation that originates in the taste buds on the tongue, distinguishes only four things—sweet, sour, salt, and bitter. The taste of roast beef or cabbage, salmon or pineapple is almost entirely due to its aroma. That's why many ordinarily flavorsome foods become tasteless when you have a bad cold.

You can easily prove how smell affects taste by eating a piece of apple while holding a more odoriferous pear close to the nostrils. Because of its stronger smell, the pear will impart its flavor to the apple.

How Stereo Pictures Fool Your Sight

You needn't depend upon ready-made stereo cameras and viewers to give you the fun of seeing pictures that seem to stand right out in space. You can observe the effect with your eyes alone and, if the subject won't move between exposures, take such pictures with an ordinary one-eyed camera.

Stereo pictures give you their astonishing illusion of depth by imitating the tricks your eyes play in ordinary two-eyed vision. Every time you look at a real object, one eye gets one view of it and the other gets a slightly different view. Your brain blends these two views into an image that seems to have solidity and depth. If the object is nearby, your eyes give you another clue to depth by turning in toward each other; the nearer the object, the more they turn in.

Stereo photography copies two-eyed vision by taking a pair of pictures side by side, usually with a camera having two lenses spaced about as far apart as your eyes. When you look at these slightly different pictures in a viewer, each eye sees only the view taken by the corresponding camera lens. Your brain combines the views, just as it does when your eyes are looking at a real object. Because near objects are closer together than distant objects in these stereo

pairs, your eyes have to turn in toward near objects. This adds to the illusion of depth.

You can take stereo pictures of still-life subjects with an ordinary camera merely by taking two pictures, the second with the camera shifted to one side. Any camera using film up to about two and one-half inches square will do. Just mount it on a tripod, take one picture with the camera a trifle left of center, then move the tripod two and one-half inches to the right and take another.

Make contact prints from the two negatives and mount them on cardboard in the sequence in which they were taken. For easy viewing, space them so that similar points on the farthest object in the two pictures are two and one-half inches apart.

To see stereo pictures in the third dimension, you must relax your eyes—as you unconsciously do in daydreaming or distant vision —so that they are directed straight ahead. The lenses in the ordinary viewer help you do this. But with a little practice you can see a stereo pair in three dimensions without a viewer.

Try with the stereo pictures shown at the top of the facing page. One simple aid is to hold two fingers between your eyes and the photographs, as shown above, placing them so that your left eye can't see the right photo and your right eye can't see the left. If you now relax your eyes, the pictures will merge.

GET ACQUAINTED WITH CHEMISTRY

Atomic Energy on Your Wrist

You don't need access to secret laboratories to get an exciting introduction to atomic energy. To witness a barrage of atomic explosions, produced as one element spontaneously changes into others, just examine the luminous figures on your wrist watch under a strong magnifying glass in a pitch-dark room.

A short-focus magnifier, such as is used for counting textile threads, will do nicely. After your eyes get adapted to the darkness, look at the numerals closely through the glass. Instead of shining with a uniform glow, as they seem to the unaided eye to do, the figures now appear as fields of flashing points of light!

What you witness is an effect of atomic disintegration. Mixed in the compound that coats the numbers is a tiny amount of radium bromide and a larger amount of some fluorescent substance like zinc sulfide. As each atom of radium disintegrates, it shoots out at terrific speed an *alpha particle*, which is really the nucleus of a helium atom. Every time an alpha particle hits a zinc sulfide molecule you get a flash of light.

It was the discovery of radium by Marie and Pierre Curie in 1898 and the study of its rays during the next few years that changed man's whole conception of atomic structure and his theories of chemistry. Before 1903, atoms were considered to be the ultimate particles of matter, and *transmutation*, or the changing of one element into another, was ridiculed as an alchemist's dream.

Lord Rutherford was the first to recognize in radioactivity a spontaneous breaking-down of the "unbreakable" building blocks of the universe. As it explodes, radium changes into helium and a gas, radon; radon, after a series of further changes, winds up as lead. From accumulated evidence, Rutherford soon formulated a new theory. According to his idea, atoms were not solid, indivisible particles but were tiny universes made up of far smaller particles

The luminosity of watch and clock dials is due to atomic explosions. Particles shot from radium hit zinc sulfide and produce flashes of light.

that whirled about, chiefly in empty space. To prove it, he shot alpha particles right through thin sheets of solid gold. He then bombarded gases with these particles and actually changed the gases into new elements. Since Lord Rutherford's time, it has been found possible to transmute *all* the elements by shattering them with high-speed particles. Modern atom-splitting techniques owe their beginning to observation of radium explosions like those that take place on your watch dial.

If you carefully neutralize a solu- tion of poisonous hydrochloric
tion of poisonous lye with a solu- acid, you produce a new com-

Poisons into Common Salt—Titration

You can easily show how acids and bases neutralize each other to form compounds that are often amazingly different from either of the original ingredients. Starting with the deadly poisons hydrochloric acid and lye (impure sodium hydroxide), you can wind up with sodium chloride, common table salt! At the same time, you can get a glimpse of the rudiments of *titration*, an important technique used by the chemist to measure acidity and alkalinity.

Dissolve about ½ teaspoonful of lye in ½ glass of water. In the laboratory, several drops of phenolphthalein solution would be added to the mixture to serve as an indicator. If you have none of this regular test solution, look at the labels of the laxatives in your medicine cabinet. You will probably discover one that contains it. Grind up a tablet or two in water and add two or three drops to your lye solution. The solution should turn pink and remain so as long as it is alkaline.

Now dilute 1 part of hydrochloric acid with 4 parts of water and

pound, which, after evaporation, turns out to be one of the most *familiar chemicals on our diet— common table salt!*

add this dilute acid, drop by drop, to the colored lye solution, stirring constantly as you do so. As acid is added, the pink becomes paler. Finally, the addition of a single drop causes the color to vanish completely. When this point has been reached, the hydrochloric acid and the lye no longer exist as individual entities. Acid has neutralized base. What remains in solution is a compound called a *salt*.

That the compound in this case is common table salt can be verified by letting the water evaporate normally or by boiling it away with heat. When all the water is gone, white crystals remain. Touch several to your tongue (never taste more than the tiniest amounts of homemade chemicals!), and your taste will recognize familiar sodium chloride.

Titration—a method of measuring the amount of acid or base in a given solution—is similarly carried out by neutralization. By noting the exact amount of a standard solution of an acid or base required to neutralize a given quantity of the solution under test, the acidity or basicity can easily be calculated.

Sugar Is Carbon and Water

Every housewife who has made caramel sauce or who has wept from the irritating fumes of sugar burning on the stove has been witness to the process of chemical decomposition. White sugar, oddly enough, is composed simply of black carbon plus the gases hydrogen and oxygen in the same proportion in which they occur in water. Heat sugar mildly, and a portion of the gases is driven off as water vapor, leaving caramel. Heat it strongly, and some of the carbon joins with the gases to form carbon dioxide, furfural, and sharp-smelling, tear-provoking acrolein. What's left this time is nothing but hard-to-remove carbon.

Because concentrated sulfuric acid has such a strong affinity for water that it can often remove it from other compounds, this acid can be used in a spectacular stunt that will also demonstrate the basic composition of sugar. Half fill a small glass with sugar, as shown below, and with a glass rod stir in enough sulfuric acid to wet it thoroughly. (Be careful not to spill the acid on hands or furnishings.) Then watch and wait. Soon the sugar darkens, boiling begins, and, finally, accompanied by clouds of steam, a cokelike column of carbon rises out of the glass to a height many times that of the original heap of sugar!

How Metals Change Places

Did you ever dip a nail or a knife blade into a solution of copper sulfate and bring it out coated with metallic copper? Here is a more spectacular sequel that demonstrates the same chemical principle. A roll of tin foil, suspended in a solution of silver nitrate, changes before your eyes into a "tree" with leaves of glittering silver!

To make this tree, dissolve ¼ ounce of silver nitrate (be careful with this; it's very corrosive) in 2 ounces of water. Pour into a 2-ounce bottle and suspend a little roll of tin foil, first cleaned by scraping with a knife, by a string from the stopper. Within a few minutes sparkling crystals of pure silver deposit themselves over the tin foil, as shown in the photograph. Your tree continues to grow until all the tin has been replaced by silver.

The reason? All metals can be arranged in a series according to the ease with which they enter into chemical reactions. Aluminum, for instance, is more active than iron; iron is more active than copper or silver; while platinum and gold are chemical sluggards. A list of the common metals, according to activity, is given at the right. Place any metal in this series in a solution of a salt of a metal that is less active (below it on the list), and the first metal dissolves, while the second comes out of solution. When a nail is put in copper sulfate, iron swaps places with less active copper, and iron sulfate and copper metal are formed. The tin, likewise, replaces an equivalent amount of silver in the silver nitrate, ousting the silver as shining crystals.

POTASSIUM

SODIUM

CALCIUM

MAGNESIUM

ALUMINUM

ZINC

CHROMIUM

IRON

NICKEL

TIN

LEAD

COPPER

MERCURY

SILVER

PLATINUM

GOLD

136

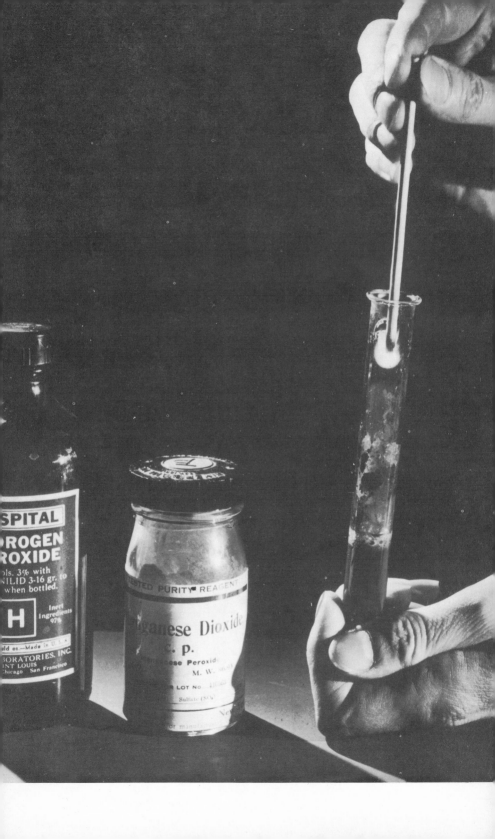

Iron and Steel Burn in Oxygen

Strange as it may seem, a gas, oxygen, is the most widely distributed and abundant of all the chemical elements. Look in the mirror and there behold a creature 65 per cent of whose weight is made up of this gas! The waters of the sea and the water you drink are nearly 89 per cent oxygen. Oxygen makes up about 21 per cent of the air you breathe. Wood, bricks, paper, glass, bread, all contain it. Oxygen in the earth's crust weighs nearly as much as all the other elements put together, including iron, lead, copper, and all the rest of the metals!

Because it is colorless, odorless, and tasteless, however, oxygen was not discovered until 1774, when Joseph Priestley, an English clergyman, placed mercuric oxide in a glass tube, focused the sun's rays on it with a burning glass, and collected the gas that was produced. He thrust a lighted candle into the new gas, and the candle flared up brighter. A mouse placed in it became frisky. Breathing some himself, he felt invigorated. Priestley straightway recommended his gas for use in medicine and for blowing into fires to make them hotter. Today his oxygen is used routinely in hospitals for treating gas poisoning and pneumonia and in oxyacetylene torches that cut through steel like butter.

With hydrogen peroxide from the medicine chest and manganese dioxide from a discarded flashlight cell, you can make oxygen and duplicate some of the experiments that thrilled its discoverer. Household hydrogen peroxide can release 10 volumes of oxygen from each volume of liquid. Manganese dioxide acts as a catalyst to help set it free. To obtain manganese dioxide, break open an old flashlight cell; the black powder inside contains it. Put an inch of peroxide in a test tube and add a few grains of the powder. Bubbles of oxygen immediately come forth, and the gas soon fills the tube. Thrust into the tube a sliver of wood or a piece of cord with a spark on its tip. The spark bursts into flame. Even iron and steel burn in this active gas. A small piece of steel wool, heated red hot, burns brightly and throws off showers of sparks when lowered into the tube.

139

Precipitation Makes Solids from Liquids

Merely by mixing two water-clear solutions, you can demonstrate one of the most important transformations in chemistry. Half fill two tumblers with water. In the first dissolve a little sodium carbonate, or washing soda; in the second a little calcium chloride, the chemical used to help dry out cellars. Now pour one solution into the other, and minute particles of solid matter form a dense white cloud (as shown at right), which gradually settles. These white particles are calcium carbonate, the precipitated chalk used in tooth powders, polishes, and medicine!

Such *precipitation* occurs every time solutions of two compounds react to form another that does not dissolve. By means of it, hundreds of chemical compounds may be produced and separated. Some antidotes for poisons render the poisons harmless by precipitating them. Water is often purified by forming in it a sticky, gelatinous precipitate, which catches suspended particles and carries them down with it. Do you want to show how this works? Add a little alum and ammonia to a glass of water containing a few drops of blue-black ink. A precipitate of aluminum hydroxide is formed which gradually drags the ink particles to the bottom.

The Mystery of the Dancing Mothballs

As part of a popular store-window attraction, little white balls ascend and descend tirelessly in a cylinder of clear liquid, while fascinated spectators try to guess what makes them dance.

If you want to set up a similar display (perhaps as a table center-piece) to mystify your friends, here's how it's done. To a tall glass or vase of water add 1 tablespoonful of white vinegar and then, slowly (to prevent bubbling over), ½ teaspoonful of bicarbonate of soda. While the mixture is still fizzing, drop in five or six ordinary mothballs. Then watch and wait. Within a minute or so, one ball after the other slowly rises to the top, hesitates there a moment, then drops to the bottom—only to repeat the process every few minutes for several hours!

What makes them tick? If you observe carefully, you will notice that bubbles of carbon dioxide (soda-water gas), released by the reaction of the vinegar and baking soda, accumulate on the surface of the balls. When the bubbles become large and plentiful enough, they buoy the balls to the surface. At the top, some get knocked off, and down go the balls to accumulate more. Mothballs do not react chemically with the solution. They are slightly heavier than it is, do not dissolve, and their rough surfaces provide nuclei on which bubbles form easily.

Watch Out for Things That "Won't Burn"!

The next time you want to bet that such-and-such a substance "absolutely won't burn," don't bet with a chemist! Many materials are indeed nonflammable under ordinary conditions; but divide these materials finely enough, mix them with the wrong companions, or apply sufficient heat—and, zowie! up they go in flame and smoke!

Carbon tetrachloride, for instance, is ordinarily so unburnable that it is used as the fluid in most small pump-type fire extinguishers; sand, too, puts out fires; and the metal, zinc, should certainly furnish poor kindling. Yet mix these three materials together, apply heat or set them off with a primer, and they burn intensely.

You can prove this in a dramatic test. Mix ½ teaspoonful of fine sand with an equal amount of zinc dust (filed, perhaps, from an old dry-cell casing) in a metal bottle cap. Then, by means of tongs, hold the cap over the flame of an alcohol lamp or cigarette lighter. When quite hot, add several drops of carbon tetrachloride (nonflammable Carbona will do). Instantly the mixture becomes white hot and gives off volumes of gray smoke. More carbon "tet," instead of diminishing the fire, intensifies it. The great heat is caused by the reaction of chlorine with the zinc; the dense smoke, by particles of carbon and vaporized zinc chloride. Similar mixtures, contained in cans and ignited by priming compounds, are used as smoke-screen producers in warfare.

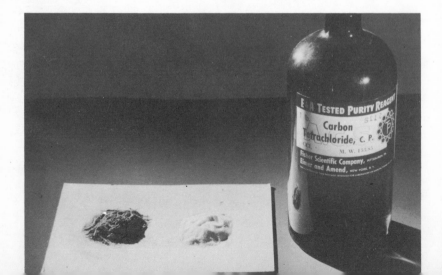

A kitchen-table version of the military "smoke pot" produces great heat and smoke from "unburnable" zinc, sand, and carbon tetrachloride.

CHEMISTRY IN THE HOME

How Soap Cleans

In the first century A.D., Pliny the Elder told his readers how to make soap from goat's tallow and beechwood ash. Yet no one knew how soap actually cleans until comparatively recent times.

Dirt clings to things chiefly because of a film of oil or grease on them which plain water can't dislodge. A notion long held was that soap dissolved this grease by releasing free alkali which made the grease soluble. Today we know that soap cleans for three reasons. By lowering the surface tension, it makes water able to wet greasy surfaces; it emulsifies this grease, enabling water to hold it in suspension; its molecules have a greater attraction for dirt particles than have the surfaces to which they were attached.

You can show how soap lowers surface tension by spilling a little water on any surface that repels water, as illustrated below. The water breaks up into globules, as at the right of the plate. Rub a finger on wet soap, however, and smear some of the globules with it. Water then wets the plate willingly, as at the left!

By putting a little household dirt mixed with a few drops of cooking oil into two glasses, as shown in the photographs at the right, you can demonstrate how soap dislodges, emulsifies, and holds dirt in suspension, so that it can readily be removed.

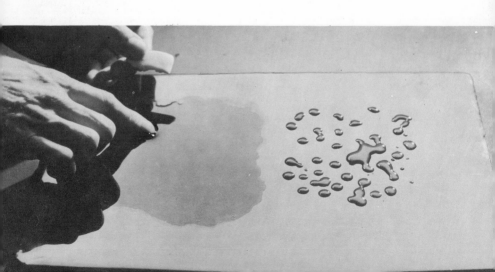

Add water to two glasses containing greasy dirt. Add soap to one glass.

Then shake both glasses and allow to stand. In the glass containing water only, dirt clings to the sides and settles on the bottom. In the other, dirt remains suspended and so may easily be rinsed out.

SOFT WATER HARD WATER HARD WATER + WASHING SODA

The Ring around the Bathtub

Hard water is a costly nuisance—especially bothersome when you try to clean things with it! Water is called "hard" when it contains more than 100 parts per million of the salts of such metals as calcium, magnesium, and iron. When soap is dissolved in hard water it reacts with these chemicals to form a curdy, insoluble substance that leaves a scum on dishes, a gray film on linens, and a ring around the bathtub. Until enough soap has been added to react with all the hardness in the water, thereby "softening" it, the soap has no power to clean.

To make cleaning easier and at the same time to save soap, water hardness is often removed chemically before soap is added. A chemical commonly used in the home for this purpose is ordinary washing soda (hydrated sodium carbonate). This forms insoluble compounds with calcium, magnesium, and iron, and causes them to fall out. Trisodium phosphate, TSP, sold also under trade names such as Oakite, is another popular household water softener.

Although it is more expensive than washing soda, the precipitates of TSP are finer and hence easier to wash away. Sodium hexametaphosphate, selling as Calgon, works on an entirely different principle. This chemical "locks up" the water hardness, forming complex compounds with it that prevent the hardness from reacting with soap or forming boiler scale yet keeping it in solution.

Comparative tests will help you to understand the differences. If you have no hard water, you can make some by adding a few grains of calcium sulfate (plaster of paris) or magnesium sulfate (Epsom salts) to a tumbler of water. Set up tumblers, as shown at the tops of these pages, the first containing soft water, the second hard water, and the rest hard water softened by the chemicals on their labels. Add a small amount of soap flakes to each glass and shake. To see how hard water can be bested without first softening it, add a little Dreft to the last glass. This new detergent contains no soap at all. It produces copious suds and cleans well because, unlike soap, it does not react with the chemicals that cause hardness.

A Test for Water Hardness

In softening water at home, too much or too little softening agent means waste. You can find out just how much you need by means of a simple suds test. Make (or have prepared at the drugstore) a soap solution by dissolving ¼ ounce of castile soap in 5 ounces of warm 80 per cent alcohol and then filtering. Now put a measured amount of distilled water into a clean bottle and add the soap solution drop by drop, shaking the water between each drop, until a foam covers the surface and remains there a minute. Next make a series of tests with hard water containing different amounts of softener. Empty the bottle between each test and always add the softening agent before the soap. You will have added the correct amount of softener when the water forms stable suds with no more soap than is required with distilled water.

Clean Your Silver by Electrolysis

Packaged chemicals, sometimes accompanied by "magic" plates or containers of aluminum, save the housewife hours of work by enabling her to clean her silverware without scouring it. Using ordinary baking soda and salt, plus any old aluminum pan, you can work the same miracle. Place the silverware in the aluminum pan so that each piece touches the pan and cover with a boiling solution of 1 teaspoonful of baking soda and another of salt to each quart of water. After several minutes, remove the silver, rinse, and polish with a soft cloth.

The silver, touching the aluminum and surrounded by the electrolyte, forms one plate of an electric cell. By the action of this cell, the tarnish of silver sulfide is first dissolved, then the sulfur is separated and the silver redeposited! As a result, less silver is removed by this type of cleaning than by ordinary rubbing. The method should not be used on so-called "French-finish" silver, however, as it may clean out the gray-toned depressions as well as the surface.

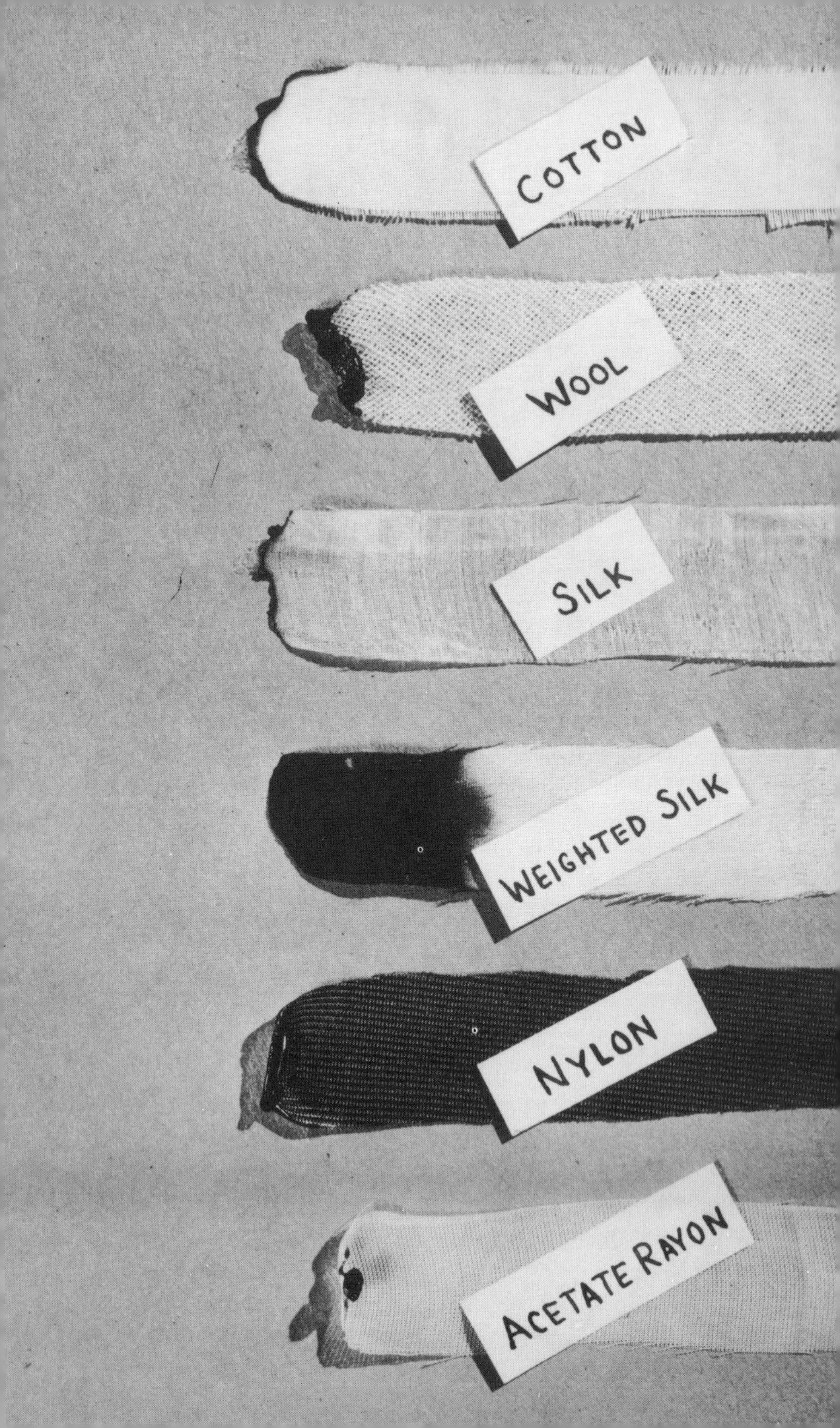

COTTON

WOOL

SILK

WEIGHTED SILK

NYLON

ACETATE RAYON

What Is That Textile?

Not many years ago, when nearly all textile materials were made of wool, cotton, linen, or silk, it was not hard for the housewife to determine by looks and feel just what her clothing, blankets, draperies, and linens were made of. Today, with dozens of new test-tube fibers competing with these natural products, it's a wise woman who knows whether her fabrics come from a field of cotton or a tree in the forest, from off a sheep's back or out of a cow's udder, from a cocoon or a glassworks!

A few simple tests, however, can often solve the mystery. Provided the fibers in a fabric are not so mixed that you can't separate them, the burning test should help you to identify some eight or ten different types of textiles. To perform it, you touch the end of a small sample to a match flame; then note the appearance of the burning, the smell, and the nature of the ash.

Cotton and linen, as well as viscose and cuprammonium rayon (the types most commonly used) all burn rapidly with the familiar odor of "burning rags" or paper. The ash is small, and after the flame goes out a glowing coal may creep along the unburned material. Because all these materials are so similar chemically, further differentiation between them must be made by appearance.

Wool and hair burn more slowly and give off an odor of burnt hair or feathers. Their ash is knobby and cokelike.

Pure silk also burns slowly, with a smell similar to that of wool, and leaves a row of cokelike beads along the edge of the fabric.

Silk that is "weighted" with metallic salts is readily discovered by the burning test. Only the silk fibers burn, leaving behind them a black ash that retains the structure of the weave.

Pure nylon doesn't burn at all, although combustible dyes or finishes may make it inflammable. It melts, though, leaving a brown mass at the edge of the material.

Acetate rayon flames and melts, producing a black ball which hardens when cold.

Glass fibers do not burn, but become red hot and may melt into tiny beads if kept long enough in a hot flame.

Are Those Pants All Wool?

Are those all-wool trousers verily what they claim to be? Snip off a tiny piece from a part that can't be seen and put it into a test tube containing a 5 per cent solution of common lye. Then boil gently for 10 or 15 minutes. If it is all wool the material will dissolve completely. If a skeleton of the fabric remains the chances are that the remainder is cotton or rayon, which are unaffected by boiling lye.

If you are still in doubt concerning a material that appears to be only part wool, give it the "acid test." Mix 2 drops of concentrated sulfuric acid with 100 drops of water and put a drop or two of this 2 per cent acid on a piece of the cloth to be proved, allowing it to sink completely through the fabric. Next, place the sample between several sheets of paper and press with a hot flatiron for a minute. If the material contains cotton, the spot where the acid was placed becomes charred. When you rub the charred spot gently between your thumb and forefinger, the cotton falls away and leaves behind it whatever wool the material contains.

Boiling lye dissolves wool from textile (left) and leaves cotton (right).

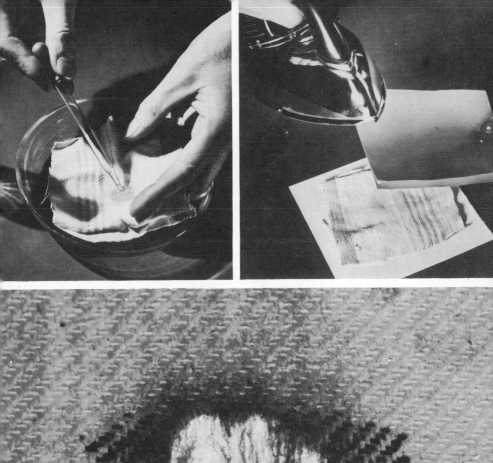

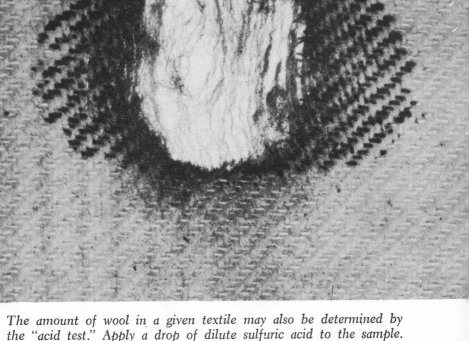

The amount of wool in a given textile may also be determined by the "acid test." Apply a drop of dilute sulfuric acid to the sample. Then press between papers with a hot iron. The cotton is charred and may be removed, leaving the wool (bottom).

The darkening of an aluminum pot may be due to iron from food.

This deposit can be removed readily by cooking acid foods in the pot.

Why Household Metals Misbehave

Aluminum is a wonderful metal—light, strong, good-looking, and not tarnished by ordinary air. Because it is more active chemically than most common metals, however, it often cuts capers in the kitchen.

That dark discoloration, for instance, which coats the inside of a pot after certain foods have been cooked in it may be due to a swapping of metals (see page 136). Perhaps you cooked oatmeal or some other food containing iron. Since aluminum is more active than iron, part of the pot went into solution, while iron from the oatmeal was deposited on the pot.

Although the neat housewife may scour away this deposit, she needn't do so, as the iron will remove itself if some acid food such as tomatoes is later cooked in the pot. In this way, too, she will regain the valuable food mineral lost from the oatmeal.

Aluminum may also be darkened by cooking in it foods containing baking soda or alkalis or by scouring it with alkaline cleansers. The color in this case is due to an impure form of aluminum oxide. It, too, may be removed by acid foods. As millions of people who use aluminum utensils constantly must eat small quantities of aluminum salts every day, apparently these salts are not harmful.

Tin is another metal that will serve you better when you get to know it. Pure tin, contrary to popular notion, is comparatively expensive (five times as costly as aluminum; three times as copper) and extremely resistant to corrosion. "Tin cans" and kitchen "tinware" are made of iron or steel with a very thin coating of tin for protection. Tinware must therefore be treated gently and cleaned only with very mild abrasives so that the surface does not get scratched. Once you break through, an electrical effect is set up between the tin and iron that causes the iron to rust faster than if it were uncoated. The popular belief that food must be removed from a tin can immediately after it has been opened has been proved groundless. Food will not spoil any faster in an open can than in any other kind of open container. Such minute amounts of tin as might be dissolved are entirely harmless.

Bleaches and Ink Eradicators

Every time you use hydrogen peroxide to remove fruit stains or chlorine to bleach clothes and take out ink, you change colored into colorless compounds by oxidizing them.

Although the less powerful of the two, hydrogen peroxide (the "peroxide" of medicine-chest and "peroxide-blonde" fame) is an important bleaching agent for silk, wool, and other materials which might be damaged by chlorine. Around the home it may be used to remove many fruit stains or the color from natural dyes. A little ammonia added to it helps release its oxygen.

Paint containing lead often darkens by reacting with traces of hydrogen sulfide in the air. Hydrogen peroxide applied to such paint restores its brightness by oxidizing the dark lead sulfide into white lead sulfate. The paintings of Old Masters have often been lightened in this way.

Chlorine compounds—particularly a 5 per cent solution of sodium hypochlorite sold under such names as Clorox, Rose-X, Dazzle, etc.—are used to bleach white cotton and linen goods, to remove dyes and stains, and to eradicate ink. Strangely enough, as was mentioned, even chlorine takes out color by *oxidation*. Chlorine reacts with water to form hydrochloric acid and unstable hypochlorous acid. The latter readily gives up its oxygen to dyes and other materials, which are thereby bleached.

Cheap sodium hypochlorite solution eradicates ink as well as more expensive solutions put up for the purpose. A drop of vinegar, applied before it, helps liberate the chlorine. Don't think for a minute, however, that ink eradicators remove all evidence of writing. The cops and your amateur chemist friends, by a second bit of chemical magic, can easily make your words reappear!

Here's how. Write a line or two with almost any ordinary ink and then "remove" it with bleach solution. Think it's gone? Just apply a blotter moistened with potassium ferrocyanide solution, and it becomes visible again! Most inks consist of a dye and iron tannate. Bleaching does not remove the iron salt but merely makes it colorless. The ferrocyanide reacts to give it color again.

When words written in ordinary iron-and-dye ink, as shown here, are

bleached out, only the color disappears; a colorless iron salt remains.

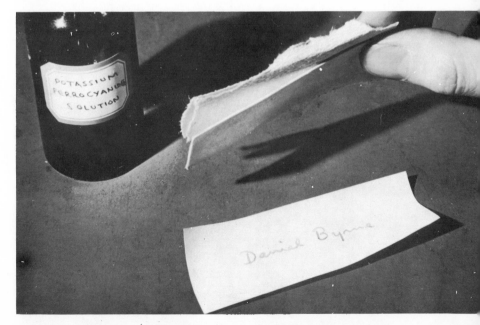

If this salt is treated chemically, the words again become visible.

CHEMISTRY IN INDUSTRY

Synthetic Oil of Wintergreen

Not many years ago the term "synthetic" was one of disparagement—a name to be flung loosely at inferior substitutes for natural commodities. It wasn't long, however, before the chemists changed all that. Today this word stands for a whole wonderland of new products—many of them superior to natural substances and some not even duplicated by nature—that are "built up" or "put together" from basic chemical building blocks. Modern plastics, nylon, dyes, perfumes, flavors, sulfa, and other miracle drugs are just a few of the better known synthetic creations.

With only a little methyl ("wood") alcohol, a mashed-up aspirin tablet, and some concentrated sulfuric acid to help speed up the reaction, you can demonstrate chemical synthesis by making methyl salicylate, man-made oil of wintergreen. Commercially, pure salicylic acid is used, but for this experiment, aspirin (acetylsalicylic acid) will serve well enough.

To about ½ inch of methyl alcohol in a test tube, carefully add about a third as much sulfuric acid. (Don't spill this on yourself,

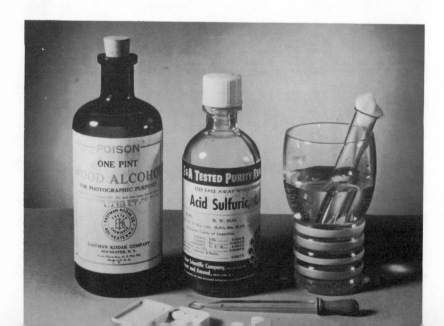

Here wood alcohol and aspirin, with sulfuric acid as a catalyst, join hands to form an entirely new product, synthetic oil of wintergreen.

your clothing, or the furniture, as it's very corrosive.) Shake gently or stir with a glass rod to mix the liquids thoroughly. Then add the powdered aspirin tablet, stir a little, stopper the tube with a loose plug of cotton, and stand the tube in a glass of warm water for 15 minutes.

At the end of that time, remove the cotton plug and smell the fumes that come from the tube. Odorless sulfuric acid has helped join odorless aspirin with alcohol to form a new substance, with the fragrant characteristic odor of oil of wintergreen!

Although you can't use your homemade product without further purification, it demonstrates the principle of synthesis vividly. Many flower odors as well as fruit odors and flavors are similarly produced—by the reaction of other alcohols with different acids.

Rayon Is Made from Trees

The miracle by which tree fibers or cotton linters are transformed into rayon fabrics is one of the greatest of modern industrial chemistry. Although complex machinery and precise control are needed to produce usable rayon yarn, you can readily demonstrate the principle of how this is done. The "cuprammonium" process—one of the three processes most widely used today—is not hard to duplicate at home. You start with a paper napkin and wind up with a rayon thread!

First you need copper hydroxide. Dissolve a scant teaspoonful of copper sulfate crystals in 3 teaspoonfuls of warm water. Then add 28 per cent ammonia solution, drop by drop, until the pale blue precipitate that results ceases to form (below left). Wash this copper hydroxide several times by shaking with water, allowing the water to settle, and pouring off the clear upper liquid; then filter it. Finally put the filtered substance into a tumbler and dissolve it in the least possible amount of ammonia.

The resulting deep blue solution (called "Schweitzer's reagent" after the German chemist who discovered it) has the unusual property of being able to dissolve paper, cotton, and other forms of cellulose. Dissolve bits of paper napkin in it until the solution becomes sirupy (below right). Fill a medicine dropper with the

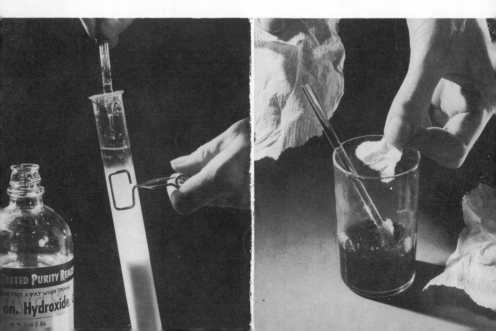

sirupy solution and squeeze it under the surface of a 5 per cent solution of sulfuric acid. The solution hardens as it leaves the dropper, forming a little worm of regenerated cellulose! Commercial rayon is extruded through much finer holes and is subsequently stretched, washed, and dried.

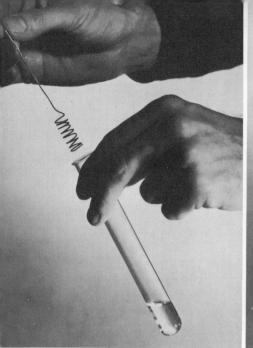 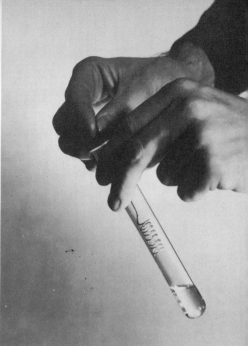

A Catalyst Helps Make Formaldehyde

By means of a catalytic oil-cracking process, chemists can now produce a superfuel superior to any gasoline hitherto available. Catalytic processes help make sulfuric and nitric acids, ammonia, dyes, alcohol, plastics, synthetic rubber, and hundreds of other chemicals. What are these catalysts, anyway?

Broadly, a catalyst is any substance that can change the speed of reaction between two or more other substances without itself being permanently changed. It is a sort of chemical parson, which joins others together yet comes out personally unharmed!

A *surface catalyst* helps join gases by holding them strongly together on its surface. Heated copper, for example, enables us thus to change methyl alcohol to formaldehyde. You can show the process easily. Wind the end of a short length of copper wire into a spiral; then gently warm a little methyl alcohol in a test tube. Now heat the spiral in a gas flame and plunge it into the alcohol vapor. The copper causes the vapor to unite with oxygen from the air and from the film of oxide on itself, and instantly the smell of wood alcohol changes to the pungent odor of formaldehyde!

Dust May Be Explosive!

Just how dust explosions occur in coal mines, grain elevators, sugar refineries, and starch factories may be demonstrated spectacularly with a candle, a small paper tube, and some cornstarch. First dry the starch by warming it for a few minutes on a radiator or over a low flame. Then put ¼ teaspoonful in the tube and with a single puff blow the powder into the candle flame. Instantly the starch bursts into a blaze of fire! Finely divided and thoroughly mixed with air, many substances that ordinarily do not burn well will burn almost as rapidly as gases. Although the small scale of the present experiment makes it harmless, a large quantity of starch dust exploding in a confined space can create a pressure wave of heated air great enough to blow out the sides of a building.

Electricity Produces Pure Copper

Refined copper for electrical conductors is, appropriately, produced by the help of electricity. With the aid of nothing but a dry cell and some copper sulfate, you can demonstrate this electrolytic magic by separating copper from zinc in a brass screw. Fasten the screw to a wire which is connected to the positive (center) terminal of the dry cell. The free end of the copper wire attached to the other terminal is bent into a grid, as shown, and both are immersed in a solution of ½ ounce of copper sulfate in 4 ounces of water. As the screw slowly disappears, pure, spongy copper is plated on the grid, while zinc from the alloy is left in solution or falls to the bottom. By careful control of the current, industry produces copper that is more than 99.9 per cent pure.

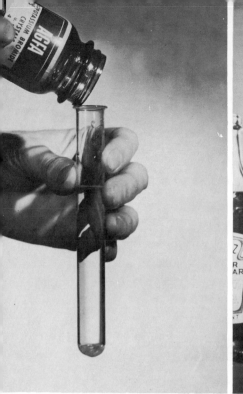

Chemicals from the Sea

In the form of ethylene dibromide, bromine extracted from the sea is now used on a huge scale to help make antiknock gasoline. As silver bromide, it is used for the sensitizing material in photographic films and papers. Potassium, sodium, and ammonium salts are the well-known "bromides" of medicine.

Although sea water contains less than 70 parts of bromine per million, methods have been found to separate it profitably. Chief aid in the separation is chlorine, which is able to oust bromine from its compounds. You can easily show how this is done. To represent sea water, dissolve a few grains of potassium bromide in a tumbler or test tube of water. Acidify this with a little vinegar. Then add a few drops of Clorox, or other cleaning fluid containing sodium hypochlorite. Instantly, released chlorine joins with the potassium and frees the bromine. The free bromine turns the solution, originally water-white, to a deep brown.

Bleaching with Sulfur Dioxide

Sulfur dioxide—the biting fumes of burning brimstone—has been used to kill germs and bugs since the days of Homer, to bleach cloth since the days of Paracelsus. Today it is used in enormous quantities to bleach paper pulp, silk, wool, straw, and other materials that might be injured by chlorine. Apricots, peaches, apples, and pears are exposed to sulfur dioxide before drying to prevent discoloration and spoilage. The sulfur dioxide unites with water to form sulfurous acid; this acid, in turn, robs oxygen from colored compounds, changing them into colorless ones.

How sulfur dioxide works can be shown by a feat of chemical magic. Put ½ teaspoonful of sodium bisulfite (a common photographic chemical) into a tall tumbler; then add a dozen drops of concentrated sulfuric acid. Although you can't see it, sulfur dioxide soon fills the glass. Because it is heavier than air, you can now pour the gas from the tumbler into a tall vase or cylinder. To prove that this empty-seeming vase is really full, pour into it a glassful of water tinted with potassium permanganate. Presto! Before the purple-colored liquid reaches the bottom of the vase it becomes colorless!

FIRE-FIGHTING CHEMISTRY

Water Is the Most Important Extinguisher

Properly controlled, fire is one of the most useful chemical reactions known to man. Manufacturing, transportation, food processing, heating, civilization itself depend upon it. When it gets out of hand, however, fire can be a terrifying destroyer.

As most big fires start with small ones, they can usually be checked and the damage minimized if they are caught early and attacked intelligently. The problems of fighting small fires are all simple problems of chemistry which can be demonstrated at home.

Every ordinary fire is the result of the rapid oxidation of some burnable material. In order for such oxidation to take place two conditions must be satisfied: first, the material must be heated to its kindling temperature; second, there must be sufficient oxygen. If we can in any way reduce the temperature or cut off the oxygen, the fire will stop. The two chief methods of fire extinguishing are, consequently, cooling and smothering. Whether one, the other, or both methods should be used depends upon the type of fire.

The oldest method of reducing the kindling temperature was to soak the blazing material with water. Even today, water is still the most effective—as well as the cheapest and most abundant—tool for putting out large fires of wood, paper, clothing, or other ordinary materials. The common soda-acid extinguisher owes most of its effectiveness to water.

Water is a good fire-fighting agent for several reasons. In the first place, it won't burn. In the second, water has the ability to absorb more heat from a hot body, weight for weight, than any other common substance. Thirdly, in boiling, water extracts a still greater amount of heat from the burning material. In fact it takes about six times as much heat to boil away 1 pound of water already at the boiling point as it does to bring 1 pound of cold water to that temperature.

 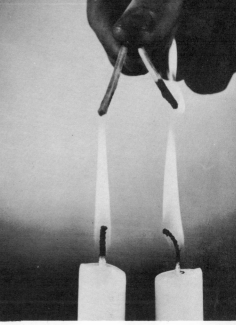

To prove that plain water is the better cooling agent, soak one matchstick in water and another in carbon tetrachloride.

Hold the matchsticks over equal flames. The water-soaked stick retards fire longer because water absorbs greater heat in boiling.

An easy experiment will prove to you that plain water can hold a given substance below its kindling point longer than can any other fire-extinguishing liquid. Soak one matchstick in water and another in carbon tetrachloride, the fluid used in pump-type hand extinguishers. When both have been equally soaked, hold them over candle flames, as shown at right above. If the race is conducted fairly, the match soaked in carbon tetrachloride will always burst into flame before the water-soaked match has begun to char. Water will win out over other liquids, too.

Don't let this prejudice you against carbon tetrachloride, however, as this chemical depends for its action upon smothering a fire rather than upon cooling it. In small fires, great cooling is not necessary. Here, the heavy, nonflammable vapor released when carbon tetrachloride boils—a vapor more than five times as heavy as air—hangs over the burning material and snuffs out the fire by cutting off its supply of oxygen. Carbon tetrachloride is also effective in stopping oil, paint, gasoline, and electrical fires, where water should never be used.

171

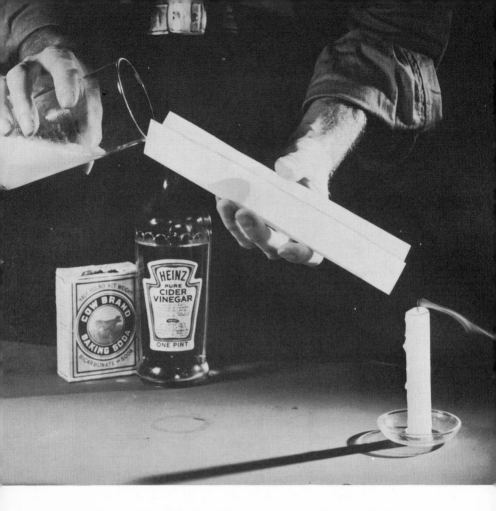

How Carbon Dioxide Puts Out Fire

Carbon dioxide, the familiar gas that makes bread rise and soda water fizz, also helps put out fires. Before being used as an extinguisher, it is liquefied under pressure and stored in thick-walled cylinders. When released, the liquid expands to form a heavy, non-burning blanket of gas.

A neat little stunt will convince you both of the weight of the gas and of its ability to snuff out fire. Put ½ teaspoonful of bicarbonate of soda (baking soda) into a large glass and add a little vinegar. Although you can't see it or smell it, carbon dioxide soon fills the glass. Then pour the gas over a candle flame. The flame goes out instantly.

For a still more impressive demonstration, pour the gas down a paper trough, as shown in the photograph on the opposite page. The heavy gas (one and a half times as heavy as air) flows down the trough as if it were water and blows out the candle.

Most dry-powder extinguishers also owe part of their ability to carbon dioxide, derived from dry bicarbonate of soda. You can demonstrate the effect of this chemical by placing a little in the end of a paper tube and blowing it suddenly onto a small fire of burning paper. If you do this properly, the fire should go out at once, as shown above. Upon being heated, bicarbonate of soda decomposes to form sodium carbonate and carbon dioxide. This reaction extracts a large amount of heat from the fire. In addition, the carbon dioxide acts as a smothering agent.

Oil fires, such as this one, must
be extinguished by smothering.

If the fire is in a pan or can,
even cardboard can put it out.

How to Put Out an Oil Fire

When paint, gasoline, grease in the frying pan, or oil in the engine
of your car starts blazing, forget all you know about water as a good
extinguishing agent. Water won't mix with oily things. Because
it is heavier than most of them, it sinks, causes them to overflow,
and thus spreads the flames.

Oil fires must be put out by smothering. Where oil is confined,
such as in a pail, can, or pan on the stove, this may be done merely
by covering the utensil with a tin pie plate or can cover. Even a
sheet of cardboard, if handled deftly, can extinguish an oil fire
which looks terrifying.

For smothering larger oil fires, carbon dioxide and methyl bromide are the most effective agents. These gases are available in
liquefied form in small extinguishing units. When sprayed onto a
fire, the liquid expands into a heavy, nonburning gas which snuffs

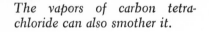

The vapors of carbon tetra-chloride can also smother it.

Put water on an oil fire, however, and this is the result!

out the flame by crowding out its oxygen. If carbon tetrachloride is used on such fires, the stream should be directed against the farther, inside surface of the container, just above the flames. There it will be scattered and vaporized into a gas to put out the blaze.

The experiments shown above will help familiarize you with this type of fire fighting. A small can, filled almost to the top with water, stands on two pie tins, back to back. A little lighter fluid or gasoline is poured on the water. Although the fire appears formidable it can be extinguished merely by sliding a piece of cardboard over the top of the can.

Carbon tetrachloride vapor can also put out a confined oil fire. Wet a wad of cotton in this chemical and hold it over the flame. As soon as the carbon tetrachloride vaporizes, the fire flickers out. Pour water on such a fire, however, and the burning fluid overflows, creating a spectacular blaze. (This will burn itself out in a few seconds if you have followed instructions.)

Fireproofing Textiles

Death and loss of property caused by fire might be sharply cut if curtains, draperies, tents, awnings, and flimsy clothing were to be made of slow-burning textiles or of ordinary materials made fire resistive by chemical treatment. Although, like wood, most textiles cannot be made completely fireproof, they can be impregnated so that they will not spread or support flames.

The effect of fireproofing can be shown by a simple test. Tear a small piece of unsized muslin into two parts. Soak one for several minutes in a solution of 1 ounce of borax and ¾ ounce of boric acid (both in crystal form) in 1 pint of water and then allow to dry. Next fasten the two pieces of cloth to the ends of an improvised wire fork, as shown in the photograph, and touch the bottom of each simultaneously to a flame. The untreated piece immediately blazes up and is consumed; the other is merely charred.

Although the solution just mentioned is cheap and effective, the salts in it are soluble and have to be reapplied after each washing. For materials that must be washed often, therefore, a two-solution process which precipitates an insoluble compound on the fibers is better. The process is as follows: Soak the cloth in a warm solution of 3 pounds of sodium stannate in 1 gallon of water. Then wring, dry, and soak the cloth in a solution of 1¼ pounds of ammonium sulfate per gallon. After wringing and drying again, rinse the cloth several times in cold water and dry once more.

Both of these treatments may be used for children's clothing, curtains, lamp shades, amateur stage scenery and props, and for party decorations where there is danger of contact with fire. To make sure that the solutions will not affect the color or other appearance of the fabric treated, test a small sample before application.

For heavy materials such as awnings, tents, or canvas car covers, another double bath is recommended by the United States Bureau of Standards. The material is first coated—either by dipping or spraying—with a solution of 2 pounds of ammonium phosphate per gallon of water and then with a solution of 3 pounds of alum

Untreated cloth burns furiously, while fireproofed material merely chars.

in 2 gallons of water. The aluminum phosphate which is formed in the cloth does not wash out readily but should probably be re-applied each season.

Since the Second World War, a number of new fireproofing substances have been made available. One is ammonium sulfamate, a water-soluble chemical which is applied by soaking or spraying. Another is chlorinated paraffin, a substance that is waterproof and mildewproof as well as flame resistive. Chemically speaking, ordinary paraffin is made up of carbon and hydrogen. By taking apart its molecules and substituting nonflammable chlorine for burnable hydrogen, chemists produce an oil or wax that won't catch fire.

INDEX

179

180

181